TIP LE

GRACE LIVINGSTON HILL
L I B R A R Y

TIP LEWIS
AND HIS LAMP

I S A B E L L A   A L D E N

LIVING BOOKS®
Tyndale House Publishers, Inc.
Wheaton, Illinois

Living Books is a registered trademark of Tyndale House
Publishers, Inc.

ISBN 0-8423-3184-0

Printed in the United States of America

01	00	99	98	97	96	
7	6	5	4	3	2	1

WELCOME

by Grace Livingston Hill

As long ago as I can remember, there was always a radiant being who was next to my mother and father in my heart, and who seemed to me to be a combination of fairy godmother, heroine, and saint. I thought her the most beautiful, wise, and wonderful person in my world, outside of my home. I treasured her smiles, copied her ways, and listened breathlessly to all she had to say, sitting at her feet worshipfully whenever she was near; ready to run any errand for her, no matter how far.

I measured other people by her principles and opinions, and always felt that her word was final. I am afraid I even corrected my beloved parents sometimes when they failed to state some principle or opinion as she had done.

When she came on a visit, the house seemed glorified because of her presence; while she remained, life was one long holiday; when she went away, it seemed as if a blight had fallen.

She was young, gracious, and very good to be with.

This radiant creature was known to me by the name of Auntie Belle, though my mother and my grandmother called her Isabella! Just like that! Even sharply sometimes when they disagreed with her: *"Isabella!"* I wondered that they dared.

Later I found that others had still other names for her. To the congregation of which her husband was pastor she was known as Mrs. Alden. And there was another world in which she moved and had her being when she went away from us from time to time; or when at certain hours in the day she shut herself within a room that was sacredly known as a Study, and wrote for a long time, while we all tried to keep still; and in this other world of hers she was known as Pansy. It was a world that loved and honored her, a world that gave her homage and wrote her letters by the hundreds each week.

As I grew older and learned to read, I devoured her stories chapter by chapter, even sometimes page by page as they came hot from the typewriter; occasionally stealing in for an instant when she left the study, to snatch the latest page and see what had happened next; or to accost her as her morning's work was done, with: "Oh, have you finished another chapter?"

Often the whole family would crowd around when the word went around that the last chapter of something was finished and going to be read aloud. And now we listened, breathless, as she read, and made her characters live before us.

The letters that poured in at every mail were overwhelming. Asking for her autograph and her photograph; begging for pieces of her best dress to sew into patchwork; begging for advice on how to become a great author; begging for advice on every possible subject. And she answered them all!

Sometimes I look back upon her long and busy life, and marvel at what she has accomplished. She was a marvelous housekeeper, knowing every dainty detail of her home to perfection. And a marvelous pastor's wife! The real old-fashioned kind, who made calls with her husband, knew every member intimately, cared for the sick, gathered the young people into her home, and loved them all as if they had been her brothers and sisters. She was beloved, almost adored, by all the members. And she was a tender, vigilant, wonderful mother, such a mother as few are privileged to have, giving without stint of her time, her strength, her love, and her companionship. She was a speaker and teacher, too.

All these things she did, and *yet wrote books!* Stories out of real life that struck home and showed us to ourselves as God saw us; and sent us to our knees to talk with him.

And so, in her name I greet you all, and commend this story to you.

Grace Livingston Hill

(This is a condensed version of the foreword Mrs. Hill wrote for her aunt's final book, *An Interrupted Night*.)

1

Cast thy bread upon the waters.

THE ROOM was very full. Children, large and small, boys and girls, and some looking almost old enough to be called men and women, filled the seats. The scholars had just finished singing their best-loved hymn, "Happy Land"; and the superintendent was walking up and down the room, spying out classes here and there which were without teachers and supplying them from the visitor's seat, which was up by the desk.

The long seat near the door was filled this morning by half a dozen dirty, ragged, barefooted boys; their teacher's seat was vacant, and those boys looked, every one, as though they had come thither just to have a grand frolic.

Oh, such bright, cunning, wicked faces as they had!

Their torn pants and jackets, their matted hair, even the very twinkle in their eyes, showed that they were the "Mission Class." That is, the class which somebody had gathered from the little black, comfortless-looking houses which thronged a narrow back street of that village, and coaxed to come to the Sabbath school—to this large, light, pleasant room, where the sun shone in upon little girls in white dresses with blue and pink ribbons fluttering from their shoulders; and upon little boys, whose snowy linen collars and dainty knots of black ribbon had evidently been arranged by careful hands that very morning.

But those boys in the corner kicked their bare heels together, pulled each others' hair, or laughed in each others' faces in the greatest good humor.

The superintendent stopped before them.

"Well, boys, good morning; glad to see you all here. Where's your teacher?"

"Hain't got none!" answered one.

"Gone to Guinea!" said another.

"She was afraid of us," explained a third. "Tip here put his foot through one of her lace flounces last Sunday. Tip's the worst boy we've got, anyhow."

The boys all seemed to think this was very funny, for they laughed so loudly that the little girls at their right looked over to see what was the matter.

Tip ran his fingers through his uncombed hair and laughed with the rest.

"Well," said the superintendent, "I'm going to get you a teacher, one you will like, I guess; I shall expect you to treat her well."

There was just one person left on the visitor's seat—a young lady who looked shy and quiet.

"Oh, Mr. Parker!" she said, when the superintendent told her what he wanted, "I can't take that class; I've watched those boys ever since they came in— they look mischievous enough for anything and act as they look."

"Then shall we leave them with nothing but mischief to take up their attention?"

"No, but—they really ought to have a better teacher than I—someone who knows how to interest them."

"But, Miss Perry, the choice lies between you and no one."

And while she hesitated and looked distressed, Mr. Parker bent forward a little and said softly:

" 'Inasmuch as ye did it not to one of the least of these my brethren, ye did it not to me.' "

The lady rose quickly and gathered her mantle about her.

"I will go, Mr. Parker," she said, speaking quickly, as if afraid her courage would fail her. "Since there is no one else, I will do the best I can; but, oh, I am afraid."

Down the long room, past the rows of neatly dressed, attentive children, Mr. Parker led her to the seat near the door.

"Now, boys," said he, "this is Miss Perry; suppose you see if you can't all be gentlemen and treat her well."

Miss Perry sat down in the teacher's chair, her heart all in a flutter; she taught a class in her own Sabbath school hundreds of miles away—five rosy-cheeked, bright-eyed little girls gathered around her every Sabbath—but they were little girls whose mothers had taught them to love their lessons, to listen respectfully to what their teacher said, to bow their heads reverently in prayer; and, more than that, they loved her, and she loved them. But these boys! Still, she must say something; six pairs of bright, roguish eyes, brimful of fire and fun, were bent on her.

"Boys," she said gently, "have you any lessons for me?"

"Not much," answered Bob Turner, who always spoke first.

"We don't get lessons mostly. Don't come unless it's too hot to go fishing or berrying."

"Tip comes 'cause he's too lazy to go past the door."

"I don't!" drawled out the boy they called Tip; "I come to get out of the sun; it's hotter than sixty down home."

"Never mind, boys," said their frightened teacher; for they were all laughing now, as though the funniest thing in the world had happened. "See here, since you have no lessons, shall I tell you a story?"

Oh yes, they were willing enough to hear a story, if it wasn't stupid.

"I'll tell you something that happened to a boy when he was about thirteen years old; his name is Robert; he told me this story himself, so you may be sure it is true.

"He said one evening he was walking slowly down the main street of the village where he lived—"

"Where was that?" asked Bob Turner.

"Oh, it was away out west. He said he felt cross and unhappy; he had nowhere in particular to go and nothing to do. As he walked, he came to a turn where two roads met. 'Now,' thought he, 'shall I turn to the left and go home and hang around until bedtime, or shall I turn to the right and go down to the river a while?'

"You see, Robert hadn't a happy home—his mother was dead, and his father was a drunkard.

"While he stood thinking, a boy came around the other corner and called out:

"'Going home, Rob?'

"'Don't know,' said Robert; 'I can't make up my mind.'

"'Suppose you come on down to our house, and we'll have a game of ball?'

"Still Robert waited. He was fond of playing ball—

that was certain—and he liked company better than to walk alone; why he should think of wandering off down to the river by himself he was sure he didn't know. Still something seemed to keep saying to him, 'Go this way—turn to the right; come, go to the river,' until he said at last:

"'No, I guess I'll take a walk this way first.'

"And he turned the corner; then he was but a few steps from the river."

"What came of the other fellow?" asked Bob.

"Why, some more boys came up just then, and he walked along with them.

"There was a large elm tree on the riverbank, and there was one particular spot under it that Robert called his seat; but he found a gentleman seated there this time; he had a book in his hand, partly closed, and he was leaning back against the tree, watching the sunset.

"He looked around as he heard Robert's step and said, 'Good evening; will you have a seat?'

"He moved along, and Robert sat down on the grass near him; then he said:

"'I heard a boy call out to another just now, "Going home, Robert?" Are you the boy?'

"'No,' said Robert; 'Hal Carter screamed that out to me just as he came round the corner.'

"'Oh, you are the one he was talking to. Well, I'll ask you the same question. *Are* you going home?'

"'No,' said Robert again; 'I have just walked straight away from home.'

"'Yes; but are you going up *there?*' And the gentleman pointed up to the blue sky.

"'That's the home I mean; I've just been reading about it; this river made me think of it. Where it says, you know, "And he showed me a pure river of water, clear as crystal"; then it goes on to describe the city with its "gates of pearl" and "street of gold," the robes and crowns that the people wear, the harps on which they play, and, after this warm day, I couldn't help thinking that one of the pleasantest things about this home was the promise, "Neither shall the sun light on them, nor any heat." Aren't you going to that home, my boy?'

"'I don't know,' Robert said, feeling very much astonished."

At this point, the superintendent's bell rang, and Miss Perry had to hasten her story.

"I haven't time, boys, to tell you all the gentleman said, but after that talk, Robert began to think about these things a great deal, and pretty soon he learned to read the Bible and to pray; that was more than fifty years ago. He is an old minister now; I have heard him preach a great many times; and he told me once he should always believe God put it into his heart to turn to the right that evening, instead of the left."

"Oh!" exclaimed Tip just here; and Miss Perry stopped.

"Joe pinched me," said Tip, to explain his part of the noise.

But their teacher felt very badly; they had not listened to her story as though they cared to hear it; they had slid up and down the seat, pulled and pinched and pricked each other, and done a great many mischievous things since she commenced; and yet now and then they seemed to hear a few words; so she kept on, because she did not know what else to do.

"Oh, Mr. Parker!" she said, when the school was dismissed and her noisy class had scrambled, some through the window and some through the door.

"Some man who understands boys ought to have had that class; I haven't done them any good, but I tried"; and there were tears in her eyes as she spoke.

"You did what you could," said the superintendent kindly; "none of us can do more."

Some loving voice ought to have whispered in that teacher's ears, "He that goeth forth and weepeth, bearing precious seed, shall doubtless come again with rejoicing, bringing his sheaves with him."

2

But other fell into good ground, and brought forth fruit.

TIP Lewis yawned and stretched, and finally opened his eyes rather late on Monday morning.

"Oh, bother!" he said with another yawn when he saw how the sun was pouring into the room. "I suppose a fellow has got to get up. I wish getting up wasn't such hard work—spoils all the fun of going to bed; but then the old cat will be to pay if I don't get around soon."

And with this he rolled out; and when he dressed, which was in a very few minutes after he tumbled out of his ragged bed, he was the selfsame Tip who had been at the bottom of most of the mischief in Miss Perry's class the day before—the very same, from the curly hair, not yet combed nor likely to be, down to the bare, soiled feet.

The bed which he had just left, so far as neatness was concerned, looked very much like Tip, and the room looked like the bed, and they all looked about as bad as dust and rags and poverty could make them look.

After running his fingers through his hair, by way of finishing his toilet, Tip made his way down the rickety stairs to the kitchen.

It seemed as though that kitchen was just calculated to make a boy feel cross. The table stood against the wall on its three legs, the tablecloth was daubed with molasses and stained with gravy; a plate with something in it which looked like melted lard—but which Tip's mother called butter—and a half loaf of bread were the only eatable articles as yet on the table; and around these the flies had gathered in such numbers that it almost seemed as though they might carry the loaf away entirely, if too many of them didn't drown themselves in the butter; over all the July sun poured in its rays from the eastern window, the only one in the room.

Tip stumbled over his father's boots and made his way to the stove, where his mother was bending over a spider of sizzling pork.

"Well," she said as he came near, "did you get up for all day? I'd be ashamed—great boy like you—to lie in bed till this time of day and let your mother split wood and bring water to cook your breakfast with."

"You cooked a little for you, too, didn't you?" asked Tip, in a saucy good-natured tone. "Where's Father?"

"Just where you have been all day so far, in bed and asleep. Such folks as I've got! I'm sick of living."

And Mrs. Lewis stepped back from the steaming teakettle and wiped great beads of perspiration from her forehead; then fanned herself with her big apron, looking meantime very tired and cross.

Yet Tip's mother was not so cross after all as she seemed; had Tip only known it, her heart was very heavy that morning. She did not blame his father for his morning nap, not a bit of it; she was only glad that the weary frame could rest a little after a night of pain. She had been up since the first gray dawn of morning, bathing his head, straightening the tangled bedclothes, walking the floor with the restless baby, in order that her husband might have quiet. Oh no; there were worse women in the world than Mrs. Lewis; but this morning, her life looked very wretched to her—she thought of her idle, mischievous boy; of her naughty, high-tempered little girl; of her fat, healthy baby who took so much of her time; of her husband, who, though she never said it to him or even to herself, yet she knew and felt was every day growing weaker; and with these came the remembrance that her own tired hands were all that lay between them and want; and it is hardly a wonder that her voice was sharp and her words ill chosen. For this mother tried to bear all her trials alone; she never went for help to the Redeemer, who said:

"Come unto me, all ye that labour and are heavy laden."

"Wah!" said Johnny from his cradle in the bit of a bedroom near the kitchen—which kitchen was all the room they had, save two tiny bedrooms and Tip's little den upstairs.

Mrs. Lewis glanced quickly toward the door of her husband's room—it was closed; then she called:

"Kitty, make that baby go to sleep!"

"Oh yes," muttered Kitty, who sat on the floor lacing her old shoe with a white cord. "It's easy to say that, but I'd just like to see you do it."

"Ah yah!" answered Johnny from the cradle, as though he tried to say, "So should I."

Then, not being noticed, he gave up pretending to cry and screamed in good earnest—loud positive yells which brought his mother in haste from the kitchen.

"Ugly girl," she said to Kitty as she lifted the conquering hero from his cradle, "you don't care how soon your father is waked out of the only nap he has had all night. Why didn't you rock the cradle! I've a notion to whip you this minute!"

"I did," answered Kitty sulkily; "and he opened his eyes at me as wide as he could stretch them."

Crash! went something at that moment in the kitchen; and with Johnny in her arms, Mrs. Lewis ran back to see what new trouble she had to meet. Tip, meantime, had been in business; being hungry, he had cut a slice of bread from the loaf and, in the act of reaching over to help himself to some butter, hit his arm against a pitcher of water standing on the corner of the table. Over it went and broke, just as pitchers will whenever they get a chance. This was too much for the tired mother's patience; what little she had vanished. She tossed the slice of bread at Tip and, as she did so, said:

"There! Take that, and be off. Don't let me see a sight of your face again today. March! this instant, or you will wish you had."

And in the midst of the din, while his mother looked after the pork, which had seized this occasion for burning fast to the spider, Tip managed to spread his slice of bread, find his hat, and make good his escape from the comfortless home.

There was an hour yet to schooltime; or, for the matter of that, he might have the whole day. Tip went to school or let it alone just as he pleased. He made his way straight to his favorite spot, the broad, deep pond, and laid himself down on its grassy bank to chat with the fishes.

"My!" he said, "how nice they look whisking about; it's cool down there, I know; they don't mind the sun. I wish I had my fish pole here; I'd have one of them shiny big fellows there for my dinner; only it's too hot to fish, and it would seem kind of mean besides to get him up here in this blazing sun. Hang me if I make even a fish get out of the water today, when it can stay in."

Of all the scholars in Miss Perry's class, the one who she would have said paid the least attention was this same boy who was lying on his face by the pond, envying the fishes. Yet Tip had heard nearly every word she said; and now, as he looked into the water which lay cool in the shade of some broad, branching trees, there came into his heart the music of those words again.

"Neither shall the sun light on them, nor any heat."

"I declare!" he said as the meaning of those words dawned upon him, "I'd like that! They'll never be too warm again; it was a pretty nice story she told us about that boy. He couldn't have had a very good time; his father was a drunkard. I wish I knew just about what kind of a fellow he was; he turned right square round after that man talked to him. Now he is a minister; I suppose lots of people like him. It must be kind of nice, the whole of it. I would like to be somebody, as true as I live, I would. I'd like to have the people say, 'There goes Tip Lewis; he's the best boy in town.' Bless me! that would be funny; I don't believe they could ever say it; they are so used to calling me the worst, they couldn't help it. What if I should reform? I declare, I don't know but I will."

And Tip rolled over on his back and looked up into the blue cloudless sky; lying there, he certainly had some of the most sober thoughts, perhaps the only really sober ones he had ever known in his life. And when at last he slowly picked himself up, turned his back upon the darting fishes, and walked toward the schoolhouse, he had in his mind some vague notion that perhaps he would be different from that time forth.

Just what he was going to do, or how to commence doing it, he didn't know; but the story, to which he had seemed not to listen at all, had crept into his heart, had commenced its work—very dimly was it working, very blindly he might grope for a while, but the seed sown had taken root.

3

Inasmuch as ye have done it unto one of the least of these my brethren, ye have done it unto me.

AROUND the corner, and far up the street from where Tip Lewis lived, there stood a large white house; not another house in the village was so beautiful as this; many a time had Tip walked slowly by the place and cast the most admiring glances on the broad green lawns and bubbling fountain, of which he caught glimpses from the road. Often he had stood outside, at the great gate, and fairly *longed* for a nearer view of that same fountain; for the truth was, though he was such a rough mischief-making—yes, a *wicked* boy, down in his heart he had a great love for beautiful things.

On this Fourth of July morning, Tip was up and abroad very early—he held a horse which had been so frightened by firecrackers that it wouldn't stand still a minute, and the owner of it gave him ten cents, with which he immediately bought firecrackers for himself and frightened the very next horse he saw. When the great cannon on the hill was fired, he got in the way just as much as he knew how, which was a great deal; he contrived to be around when the largest bell was rung and add his voice to the uproar among the boys who were gathered around the church doors; indeed, wherever there was commotion or confusion, Tip managed very soon to be and to do his part toward making the most of it.

About ten o'clock he had lived out the most of his pleasures, having been on hand since a little after three. He had no more money to spend and saw no chance of getting any more; he had had no breakfast and was very much in doubt as to whether he would get any if he took the trouble to go home; he had some way lost track of all his companions, and, altogether, he was beginning to feel as if the Fourth of July were a humbug—he felt ill-used, angry; it seemed to him that he was being cheated out of a good time that he expected to have. He sat down on the edge of an old sugar barrel and thought about it awhile; then finally, with his hands in his pockets and whistling "Yankee Doodle" in honor of the day, he sauntered along the street in search of something to take up his time.

Hurrying toward him, with hands not in his pockets but full of packages, came Mr. Minturn, the owner of the grand white house on the hill.

To Tip's surprise, the gentleman halted suddenly before him and, eyeing him closely, asked:

"Whose boy are you?"

"John Lewis's."

"Where do you live?"

"T'other side of the pond, by the mill."

"Oh, your father is the carpenter, I suppose—I know him. What's your name?"

"Tip."

"Tip! What kind of a name is that; is it all the one you own?"

"Well," said Tip, "I suppose my name was Edward

when I was a little shaver; but nobody knows it now; I don't myself."

"Well, Tip, then, I'll call you that, for I want you to know yourself tonight. What are you going to do?"

"When, tonight? Oh, hang around, I s'pose—have some fun, if I can find any."

"Fun. Is that what you're after? You come up to my house tonight at dark and see if you can find it there—we are going to have fireworks, and songs, and all the fun we can."

Tip was not by any means a bashful boy, and it took a great deal to astonish him; but this sudden invitation almost took his breath away—the idea that Mr. Minturn had actually invited *him,* Tip Lewis, to come to the white house; to come near to that wonderful fountain, near enough perhaps to feel the dash of its spray—he could have danced for joy, yet when Mr. Minturn said, "Well, will you come?" for the first time in his life, Tip was known to stammer and hesitate.

"I-I don't—know, I haven't got any clothes."

"Clothes!" repeated Mr. Minturn; "what do you call those things which you have on?"

"I call 'em *rags,* sir," answered Tip, his embarrassment gone and the mischief twinkling back into his face again.

Mr. Minturn laughed and looked down on the torn jacket and pants.

"Not a bad name," he said at last. "But you've got water at your house, haven't you?"

"Lots of it."

"Then put your head into a tub of it, and bring a clean face up to my house tonight, and we'll try and find that fun you're looking for."

And Mr. Minturn, who had spent a great deal of

time for him, was passing on. "See here," he called, after he had moved forward a few steps, "if you see any boy raggeder than you are yourself, bring him along—bring every boy and girl you meet who haven't anywhere else to go."

"Ho!" said Tip, as soon as the gentleman was at safe distance, "if this isn't rich, then I don't know—fireworks in that great yard, pretty near the fountain maybe, and lots of fun. We can take anybody we like. I know what I'll do. I'll hunt up Bob Turner; his jacket has got enough sight more holes in it than mine has. Oh, ho! ain't it grand, though?" And Tip clapped his hands and whistled; and at last finding that didn't express his feelings, said, "Hurrah!" in a good strong tone.

Yes, hurrah! Tip is right; it is glorious to think that one man out of his abundance is going to open his heart and gather in God's poor, and, for one evening at least, make them happy.

God bless Mr. Minturn!

Never had the good man's grounds entertained such a group as, from all quarters of the large town, gathered before it was quite dark.

Ragged boys and girls! If those were what he wanted, he had them, sure enough, of almost every age and size. There were some not so ragged; some in dainty white dresses and shining jackets; but they went down and mingled with the others—brothers and sisters for that night at least—and were all, oh, *so* happy!

How they *did* dance and laugh and scream around that fountain, and snap torpedoes and firecrackers, and shout with wild delight when the rockets shot up into the sky, or the burning wheels spun round and round, scattering showers of real fire right in among the crowds of children!

Well, the evening hasted away; the very last rocket

took its bright, rushing way up into the blue sky, and Mr. Minturn gathered his company around the piazza with the words:

"Now, children, Mr. Holbrook has a few words to say to you, and after that, as soon as we have sung a hymn, it will be time to go home."

Mr. Holbrook was the minister; many of the children knew him well, and most of them were ready to hear what he had to say, because they knew by experience that he was old enough and wise enough not to make a long, dry speech after nine o'clock on the Fourth of July.

Only Tip, as he turned longingly away from the last dying spark of the rocket, muttered, "Bother the preaching!"

Mr. Holbrook came forward to the steps as the boys and girls gathered around him.

"Children," said he, "we have had a good time, haven't we?"

"Yes, sir!" came in a loud chorus from many voices.

"Yes, I thought you acted as though you felt pretty happy; now this has been a busy day, and we are all tired, so I'm not going to keep you here to make a speech to you; I just want to tell you, in as few words as I can, what I have been thinking about since I stood here tonight. I have watched you as you frolicked around that fountain—so many young, bright faces, all looking so happy—and I said to myself, When the time comes for us to gather around that fountain of living water which is before the throne of God, I wonder if *one* of these boys and girls will be missing— *one* of them? Oh, children, I pray God that you may *all* be there, *every* one."

Just a little speech it was—so little that the youngest

there might almost remember the whole of it—yet it meant *so* much.

Tip Lewis had wedged his way in among the boys until he stood very near the minister, and his face wore a sober, thoughtful look: it was only two days since his long talk with himself at the pond. Fourth of July, with all the merrymaking and mischief that it brought to him, had nearly driven sober thoughts from his mind, but the minister's solemn words brought back the memory of his half-formed resolves, and again he said to himself he believed he would reform; this time he added that if he knew about *how* to do it, he would begin right away. He felt it more than ever when the sweet voices of many children floated out on the evening air as they sang:

> "I have read of a world of beauty,
> Where there is no gloomy night,
> Where love is the mainspring of duty,
> And God is the fountain of light.

> "I have read of the flowing river,
> That bursts from beneath the throne,
> And beautiful flowers that ever
> Are found on its banks alone.
> I long—I long—I long to be there!"

If somebody had only known Tip's thoughts as he stood there listening to the beautiful Sabbath school hymn! If somebody had only bent down to him and whispered a few words, just to set his poor wandering feet onto the narrow way, how blessed it would have been! But nobody did.

Ah, never mind! God knew and took care of him.

4

Those that seek me shall find me.

MRS. Lewis's room was in order for once; swept, and even dusted; the cookstove cooled off, and the green paper curtain at the window let down to shut out the noise and dust; it was quiet there, too.

Kitty stood in the open door, her face and hands clean, hair combed, and dress mended; stood quite still and with a sober face, unmindful for once that there were butterflies to chase and flies to kill all around her. In the only comfortable seat in the room, a large old-fashioned armchair, sat the worn, wasted frame of Kitty's father. There was a look of hopeless sadness settled on his face. Neither Tip nor his mother were to be seen. One or two women were moving through the house with quiet steps, bringing in chairs and doing little thoughtful things in and about that wonderfully orderly room.

On the table was that which told the whole story of this unusual stillness and preparation. It was a pine coffin, very small and plain; and in it, with folded hands and brown hair rolled smoothly back from his baby forehead, little Johnny lay, asleep. Somebody, with a touch of tenderness, had placed a just-budding rose in the tiny white hand, and baby looked very sweet and beautiful in his narrow bed. Poor little Johnny! His had been a sad, neglected babyhood; many weary hours had he spent in his cradle, receiving only cross looks from Kitty, and neglected by the mother, who, though she loved Johnny and even because she loved him, must leave him to work for her daily bread. But it was all over now; Johnny's cries would never disturb them again; Johnny's weary little body rested quietly in its coffin; Johnny's precious self was gathered in the Savior's arms.

Tip came out of the bedroom and softly approached the coffin; his hair, too, was partly combed, and some attempt had been made to put his ragged clothes in order. His heart swelled, and the tears gathered in his eyes as they rested on the baby.

Tip loved his little brother, and though he had not had much to do with him, yet he had this much to comfort him—Johnny had received only kindness and good-natured words from him, which was more than Kitty could say. As she stood there in the door, it seemed to her that every time she had ever said cross, naughty words to the poor baby, or turned away from his pitiful cry for comfort, or shook his little helpless self, came back to her now—stood all around his coffin and looked straight at her. Poor Kitty thought if he could *only* come back to them for a little while, she would hold him in her arms all night without a murmur.

People began to come in now from the lowly houses about them and fill the empty chairs. Mrs. Lewis came out from the bedroom and sat down beside the armchair, thankful that her tear-stained face and swollen eyes were hidden by the thick black veil which some thoughtful neighbor had sent for her use.

In a few minutes a dozen or more people had filled

up the vacant spaces in the little room, and Mr. Holbrook arose from his seat at the coffin's head.

Tip turned quickly at the first sound of his voice and listened eagerly while he read from the book in his hand, "'And I saw the dead, small and great, stand before God.'" Listening until the closing sentence was read, "'And there shall be no more death; neither sorrow, nor crying, neither shall there be any more pain: for the former things are passed away.'"

Tip had never paid such close attention to anything in his life as he did to Mr. Holbrook's words; after that they were very simple and plainspoken, so that a child might understand them, and were about heaven, that beautiful city of which Tip had heard and thought more during the last three weeks than he ever had in his life before. His heart had been in a constant struggle with Satan ever since that morning in the Sabbath school. He didn't know enough to understand that it was Satan's evil voice which was constantly persuading him that he could not be anybody, that he was only a poor, miserable, ragged boy, with nobody to help him, nobody to show him what to do, that he might as well not try to be anything but what he was; and he didn't know either that the other voice in his heart which struggled with the evil counsel, which said to him, "Other boys as poor and ignorant as you are have reformed; that Robert did about whom the teacher told you; and then if you don't, you will never see that river nor the fountain, nor the streets of gold," was the dear, loving voice of his Redeemer.

Now, as he listened to Mr. Holbrook and heard how Johnny, little Johnny, whom he loved, had surely gone up there to be with Christ forever, and how Jesus, looking down on the father and mother and the children who were left, said to them, "I want you, too, to give me your hearts, so that when I gather my jewels I may come for you," the weak, struggling resolves in his heart grew strong, and he said within himself, while the tears fell slowly down his cheeks, *I will; I'll begin today.*

The coffin lid was screwed down, and Johnny's baby face shut out from them forever. A man came forward and took the light burden in his arms and bore it out to the wagon; down the narrow street they drove to the burial ground, which was not far away. They laid Johnny down to sleep, under the shade of a large old tree; and the grass waved softly, and the birds sang low, and the angels surely sang in heaven, because another little form was numbered among the thousands of children who stand "around the Throne."

The people moved slowly from the grave; all but Tip; he didn't want to leave Johnny; he wanted to follow him, and he didn't know how. Mr. Holbrook glanced back at the boy standing there alone, paused a moment, then, turning back, laid his hand gently on Tip's shoulder.

"You can go up there, too, my boy, if you will," he said in a low, kind tone.

Tip looked up quickly, then down again; he wanted to ask how, what he should do; but his voice choked, he could not speak a word; and with the earnest sentence, "God bless you, my little friend, and lead you to himself," Mr. Holbrook turned and left him.

Tip wandered away into the woods for a little; when he returned, the earth was heaped up fresh and black over the new mound, and Johnny was left underneath it all alone. Tip walked around it slowly, trying to take in the thought that the baby was lying there; that they should never see him again; trying, a moment after, to take in the thought that he was not there at all but had gone up to the beautiful world which the hymn told about; then he thought of the chorus and almost felt it, "I long, I long, I long to be there."

Tip had heard people pray; he had been to Sabbath school often enough to catch and remember most of the words of the Lord's Prayer; he knew enough of God to understand that he could hear prayer, and that his help must be asked if one wanted to get to heaven. He hesitated a moment, glanced half-fearfully around him—no one was there, no one but himself, and Johnny, lying low at his feet, and God looking down upon him; presently he knelt down before the little grave and began:

"Our Father which art in heaven, hallowed be thy name, thy kingdom come—" Then he stopped. Tip was in earnest now; he did not understand that prayer: he felt as though he was not saying what he meant; he commenced again:

"Oh, Jesus, I want—" Then he waited a minute. What did he want? "I want to be different; I'm a wicked boy. I want to go where Johnny is when I die; do show me how!"

Did Jesus ever fail to hear such a prayer as that— simple, earnest, every word of it *felt? Never*—and he never will.

Tip rose up from that spot, feeling that something was different. Aye, and always would be different; the Savior had reached down and taken hold of the young seeker's hand, and would forever after lead him up toward God.

5

Thy word is a lamp unto my feet.

THE SABBATH morning sun awoke Tip from a heavy sleep. He lay still a few moments, thinking who he was. Things were different; he was not simply Tip Lewis, a ragged little street boy, any longer—this was the morning when he was going to start out under a new motto, with Jesus for his guide.

He was going to Sabbath school. He had not been since the morning that Miss Perry had taught the class and told the story which was to be a blessing to him through all his future life. His evil spirit had been strong upon him during the three Sabbath mornings that had passed since then and persuaded him to stay away from the school; but this morning he was resolved to go. He had a secret hope that he should see Miss Perry again, for he did not know that she was hundreds of miles away from that village and would probably never be there again; all he knew was that a gentleman had brought her to the door and introduced her to the superintendent as Miss Perry; that much he had heard as he sat gazing at them.

This morning he judged by the sun that it was pretty late, yet he didn't get on very fast with the business of dressing; he sat down on the foot of the bed and looked sorrowfully at his jacket; he even turned it inside out to see if it wouldn't improve its appearance; but he shook his head and speedily turned it back again.

If he "only had a collar," he said to himself—"a smooth white collar, to turn down over the worn-out edges—it would make things look *so* much better." But that was something he had never had in his life, and he put on the old ragged brown jacket with a sigh. Then he put on his shoes and took them off again; the question was, which looked the best—shoes which showed every one of his toes peeping out on the top, or no shoes at all. Suddenly, a bright idea struck him—if his feet were only white and clean, he thought they would certainly look much better. Down he went to the rickety pump in the backyard, and face, hands, and feet took such a washing as they had never received before; then the old comb had to do duty. Tip had never had such a time getting dressed; but, some way, he felt a great longing this morning to make himself look neat; he had a feeling that it was ever so much more respectable to be neat and clean than it was to go looking as he had always done. Still, to carry a freshly washed face and hands, and smooth hair, was the very best he could do, and if he had but known it, these things made a great improvement.

He made his way half shyly into the mission seat, for the truth was he did not know just how the boys would receive his attempt at respectability; but he had no trouble, for several of his companions had seen his face when he took his last look into that little coffin the day before, and they felt sorry for him.

No Miss Perry appeared; and it seemed, at first, that the mission boys were to have no teacher. It was a warm morning, and the visitor's seat was vacant.

But there was at last a great nudging of elbows and whispers of "Look out now!" "We're in a scrape!" "No chance for fun today!" And only Tip's eyes looked glad when Mr. Holbrook halted before their class with, "Good morning, boys." Then, "Good morning, Edward, I am glad to see you here today"; and the minister actually held out his hand to Tip. Mr. Holbrook never called him Tip; he had asked him one morning what his real name was and since then had spoken it, "Edward," in clear, plain tones.

It was a restless, wearying class. It required all Mr. Holbrook's wits and wisdom to keep them in any sort of order, to gain any part of their attention. Yet it was not as bad as usual; partly because the minister knew how, if anybody did, to teach just such boys, and partly because Tip, hitherto the spirit of all the mischief there, never took his eyes from the teacher's face. Mr. Holbrook watched his close attention and took courage. When the other scholars had left, he laid his hand on Tip's arm with the words, "You have been a good listener today, Edward. Did you understand the story I told, of the boy who started on a journey to the Holy Land?"

"Some of it I did; you meant that he started for heaven."

"You understand it, I see. Don't you want to take that journey?"

"I mean to, sir."

"Help thou mine unbelief," was Mr. Holbrook's prayer just then; he had hoped for, longed for, prayed for these boys, especially for this one since the day before; yet he was astonished when he received the firm prompt answer, "I mean to, sir." Astonished, as too many are, that his prayer was heard.

"Have you started, my boy?" he asked, speaking with a little tremble in his voice.

"Yes, sir, I've tried; I told God last night that I would, but I don't much know how."

"You want a lamp, don't you?"

"A what, sir?"

"A lamp. You remember in the story the boy found dark places every little way; then he took out his lamp so he wouldn't lose the road. Don't you need it?"

"I want some help, but I don't know as a lamp would do me any good."

"Ah yes; the one I mean will surely help you if you give it a chance." Mr. Holbrook took from his pocket a small, red-covered book and held it up. "Do you know what book this is?" he asked.

"It's a Bible, ain't it?"

"Yes. Have you ever read in the Bible?"

"Some, at school."

"You know, then, that God told men just what to say, and they wrote it here, so you see that makes it God's words; that is what we call it sometimes—the Word of God. Now let me show you something." He turned the leaves rapidly, then pointed with his finger to a verse; and Tip read—" 'Thy word is a lamp unto my feet.' "

"Oh!" he said with a bright look; "that is the kind of lamp you mean."

"That is it; and, my boy, I want you to take this for your lamp. There is no place on the whole road so dark but that it can light you through, if you try it. When you don't understand it, there is always Jesus to go to, you know." And taking out his pencil, Mr. Holbrook wrote on the flyleaf in plain, round letters, "Edward Lewis." Then, handing the book to him with a bow and smile, the minister turned away.

Tip walked out of the school and down the road, holding his treasure closely. Such a queer, new feeling possessed him. Things were really to be different, then. The minister had talked with him, had shaken hands with him, and had given him a Bible. And here he was walking quietly away from the school, all alone, instead of leading a troop of noisy boys, intent on mischief.

"Oh, Tip Lewis!" he said to himself as he hugged his book, "I don't know but you will be somebody after all; you mean to try with all your might, don't you? and you've got a lamp now!"

6

*I will instruct thee and teach thee in the way which thou
shalt go: I will guide thee with mine eye.*

"WHY," said Tip, as he sat on the foot of the bed,
turning over the leaves of his Bible, "why, that is the
very thing I want. 'I will instruct thee and teach thee
in the way which thou shalt go.' Yes, that's exactly it. I
want to begin today and do every single thing so
different from what I ever did before that nobody will
know me. Now, if he'll help me, I can do it. I'll learn
that verse."

The verse was repeated many times over, for Tip
was not used to study. While he was busy thus, the
Spirit of God put another thought into his heart.

"I must ask Christ to help me now," he said with
reverent face; and kneeling down, he made known his
wants in very simple words and in that plain, direct
way which God loves. Then he went downstairs,
prepared for whatever should befall him that day.

Kitty was up and rattling the kitchen stove.

"Kitty, what's to pay?" Tip asked as he appeared in
the door.

"What's to pay with you? How did you happen to
get up?" Receiving no answer to this, she continued,
"The old cat is to pay—everywhere—and always is!

These nasty shavings are soaked through and through, and the wood is rotten, and there isn't any wood—anyway—and I can't make this fire burn to save my life. Mother is sick in bed—can't sit up at all. She told me to make a cup of tea for Father, and things look as if it would get made some time next month."

Kitty was only twelve years old, but, like most of those children who have been left to bring themselves up and pick up wisdom and wickedness wherever they are to be found, she was wonderfully old in mind, and was so used to grumbling and snarling that she could do it very rapidly.

"Oh!" said Tip to himself, drawing a long breath, "what a place for me to commence in!" Then he came bravely to Kitty's aid.

"See here, Kitty, don't make such a rattling; you'll wake Father. I can make this fire in a hurry. I have made one out of next to nothing lots of times; you just put some water in the teakettle, and we'll have a cup of tea in a jiff."

Kitty stood still in her astonishment and watched him while he took out the round green sticks that she had put in and laid in bits of dry paper and bits of sticks—laid them in such a careless, uneven way that it seemed to her they would never burn in the world; only he speedily proved that they would by setting fire to the whole, and they crackled and snapped in a most determined manner and finally roared outright.

Certainly, Kitty had never been so much astonished in her life. First, because that rubbish in the stove had been made to become such a positive fire; second, that Tip had actually set to work without being coaxed or scolded and made a fire!

There was a queer, new feeling about it all to Tip himself; for, strange as it may seem, so entirely selfish had been this boy's life that this was actually the first time he had ever, of his own free will, done anything to help the family at home. His spirits rose with the effort.

"Come, Kitty," he said briskly, "here's your fire; now let's fly round and get Father and Mother some breakfast. Say, do you know how to make toast?"

"It's likely I do," Kitty answered shortly. "If you had roasted your face and burnt your fingers as often as I have, making it for Father, I guess you would know how."

"Well, now, just suppose we make two slices, one for Mother and one for Father, and two cups of tea. My! you and I will be jolly housekeepers, Kitty."

"Humph!" said Kitty contemptuously.

You see, she wasn't in the least used to being good-natured, and it took a great deal of coaxing to make her give other than short, sharp answers to all that was said. But for all that, she went to work after Tip had poured some water in the dingy little teakettle and set it over the fire, cutting the two slices of bread and getting them ready to toast when there should be any coals.

Tip, meantime, hunted among the confusion of all sorts of things in the cupboard for two clean plates and cups.

"You're taken with an awful clean fit, seems to me," Kitty said as she stood watching him while he hunted for a cloth, then carefully wiped off the plates.

"Yes," answered Tip good-naturedly; "I'm going to try it for a spell and find out how things look after they are washed."

Altogether it was a queer morning to both of them; and each felt a touch of triumph when at last the toast lay brown and nice, a slice on each plate, and the hot tea, poured into the cups, smelled fresh and fragrant. The two children went softly to the bedroom door in time to hear their father say:

"What makes you try to get up if your head is so bad?"

"Oh, what makes me! What else is there for *me* to do? The young ones are both up, and if I find the roof left on the house I'll be thankful. I never knew them to stay together five minutes without having a battle."

At almost any other time in her life these words would have made Kitty very angry; but this morning she was intent on not letting her tea spill over on the toast and so paid very little attention to them.

Tip marched boldly in with his dish, Kitty following.

"Lie still, Mother, till you get some of our tea and toast, and I reckon it will cure you."

Mrs. Lewis raised herself on one elbow, saw the beautiful brown slices, caught a whiff of the fragrant tea, then asked wonderingly:

"Who's here?"

"Kitty and me," Tip made answer, proudly and promptly.

Something very like a smile gathered on Mrs. Lewis's worn, fretful face.

"Well, now," she said, "if I ain't beat—it's the last thing on earth I ever expected you to do."

What spell had come over Tip? Breakfast was a great success. After it was over he found a great many things to do—the rusty old ax was hunted up, and some hard knots made to become very respectable-looking sticks of wood, which he piled in the wood box. Kitty, under the influence of his strange behavior, washed the dishes and even got out the broom and swept a little.

Altogether that was a day long to be remembered by Tip; a day in which he began his life afresh. He made some mistakes; for he fancied, in his ignorance, that the struggle was over—that he had only to go forward joyfully over a pleasant road.

He found out his mistake; he discovered that Satan had not by any means given him up; that he must yet fight many hard, hard battles.

7

Fear not: for I have redeemed thee.

"THEY must have had an earthquake down at Lewis's this morning," Howard Minturn said to the boys who were gathered around the schoolroom door. "The first bell has not rung yet, and there comes Tip up the hill."

Up the hill came Tip, sure enough, with a firm, resolute step. The summer vacation was over. The fall term was to commence this morning, and among the things which Tip had resolved to do was this one, to come steadily and promptly to school during the term, which was something that he had never done in his life. The public school was the best one in the village, so he had the best boys in town for school companions, as well as some of the worst.

"Hallo, Tip!" said Bob Turner, coming partly down the hill to meet him; "how are you, old fellow?"

Bob had been away during most of the vacation and knew nothing of the changes which there had been in his absence. Tip winced a little at his greeting; shivered a little at the thought of the temptation which Bob would be to him.

The two had been linked together all their lives in every form of mischief and wrong—they seemed almost a part of each other—at least they *had* seemed so until within these few weeks. Now, Tip *felt* rather than knew how far separated they must be.

The bell rang, and the boys jostled and tumbled against each other to their seats.

Bob Turner, as usual, seated himself beside Tip; but then Bob only came to school about two forenoons in a week, so perhaps they might get along.

When the Bible reading commenced, Tip hesitated, and his face flushed; he had never owned a Bible to read from before, but this morning his new one lay in his pocket—the question was, Had he courage to take it out? "What would the boys think? What would they say? How should he answer them?"

He began to think he would wait until tomorrow morning; then he grew hot and ashamed as he saw that he was already trying to hide his colors. Suddenly he drew out his Bible and began very hurriedly to turn the leaves.

Bob heard the rustling and, glancing around, puckered his lips as if he were going to whistle and, snatching the book, read the name which Mr. Holbrook had written therein; then he whispered, "You don't say so! When did we steal a Bible and turn saint?"

The blood growing hotter and redder in Tip's cheeks was his only answer; but he felt that his temptation had begun. The next thing was to read; when he had finally found the place, even though there were more than fifty voices reading those same words, yet poor Tip imagined that his would be louder than all the rest, and he choked and coughed, and made more than one trial before he forced his voice to join, even in a whisper, at the words, "And they clothed him with purple, and platted a crown of thorns, and put it about his head."

It did not help him in his reading that Bob made his lips move with the rest, but said, loud enough for him to hear:

> *"The man in the moon*
> *Came down too soon,"*

and continued to repeat some senseless or wicked rhymes through the reading of the beautiful chapter.

How thankfully Tip bowed his head that morning; his heart had taken in some of the sweet words. That sacred head had been crowned with thorns, indeed—but he knew it was crowned with glory now—and he knew that Christ had suffered and died for him! He joined with his whole heart in Mr. Burrows's prayer; and though Bob pulled his hair and tickled his foot and stepped on his toes, the bowed head was not lifted, and his spirit gathered strength.

But Tip never forgot the trials of that day, nor the hard work which he had to endure them. Bob was, as usual, overflowing with mischief and, failing in finding the willing helper which he had expected in his old companion, took revenge in aiming a great many of his pranks at him. Such senseless, silly things as he did to annoy! Tip spread his slate over with a long row of figures which he earnestly tried to add, and having toiled slowly up the first two columns, Bob's wet finger was slyly drawn across it, and no trace of the answer so hardly earned appeared.

Then, too, he had his own heart to struggle against; he was so used to whispering to this and that boy seated near him, to eating apples when the teacher's back was turned, to making an ugly-looking picture on a piece of paper and pinning it on the back of a small boy before him. He was so unused to sitting still and trying to study.

What hard work it was to study, anyway! It seemed to him that he could never get that spelling lesson in the world; the harder he tried, the more bewildered he grew; a dozen times he spelled the two words, receive and believe, standing so closely together, each time sure he was right, and each time discovering that the *i*'s and *e*'s must change places; he grew utterly provoked and disheartened, and would have fairly cried had not Bob been beside him to see the tears and grow merry over them.

Finally, he lost all patience with Bob and, turning fiercely to him, after he had for the third time pitched the greasy old spelling book upside down on the floor, said:

"Look here, now, if you come that thing again, I'll pitch you out the window quicker than a wink!"

"Edward Lewis marked for whispering," said Mr. Burrows. "Edward, you have commenced the term as usual, I see; the first one marked for bad conduct."

How Tip's ears burned! How untrue it was! He had not commenced this term as usual; how differently he had tried to commence it, only he and God knew. And now to fail thus early in the day! His head seemed to spin and his brain reel; he bowed himself on the seat again, but Bob's head went down promptly, and he whispered:

"Little Bo Peep has lost her sheep—"

How often Tip had thought such things as these so very funny that he could not possibly help laughing; how silly and meaningless—yes, and cruel—did they seem to him now! Oh, Satan was struggling for Tip today; he was reaping the fruits of long weeks spent in evil company and folly.

He looked over to the back seats where sat Howard Minturn and Ellis Holbrook, hard at work on their algebra lesson, nobody thinking of such a thing as disturbing them, and, as he looked, sighed heavily. If he had only gained such a place as they had in the school, how easily he could work today. They were very little older than he—yet here he was trying to do an example in addition, doing it over four times before it was right—and they were at the head of the class in algebra. If he could only jump to where they were and go on with them! And the hopelessness of this thought made his spelling lesson seem harder: so it was no wonder, when the class formed and he took his old place at the foot, that he stayed there and spelled believe *e-i* after all; nobody was surprised, but nobody knew how very, *very* hard he had tried.

The long day, crowded full of trouble and temptation to poor Tip, wore away. At recess he wandered off by himself, trying hard to get back some of the strong, firm hopes of the morning.

One more sharp trial was in store for him. Toward the close of the afternoon Bob's fun took the form of paper balls, which, at every turn of Mr. Burrows's back, spun through the room in all directions; two or three of the smaller scholars joined him, and a regular fire of balls was kept up. The boys complained; Mr. Burrows scolded.

At last he spoke this short, prompt sentence: "The next boy I catch throwing paper, or anything else, in this room today, I shall punish severely; and I shall expect any scholar who sees anything of this kind going on to inform me."

Not five minutes after that, Mr. Burrows bent over

his desk in search of something within, when—*whisk!*
went the largest paper ball that had been thrown that
day and landed on the teacher's forehead. Some of the
scholars laughed, some looked grave and startled, for
Mr. Burrows was a man who always meant what he
said.

"Does anyone know who threw that ball?" he
asked, closing his desk and speaking in a calm, steady
tone.

No reply—silence for a minute. Then, "Ellis
Holbrook, do you know who threw that ball of
paper?"

"Yes, sir."

"Very well; I am waiting to be told."

"Tip Lewis threw it, sir."

This was a little too much for Tip. The first time in
his life that he had ever been in school all day without
throwing one, to be so accused. He sprang up in his
seat with fire in his eyes:

"I didn't!" he almost screamed. "He knows I didn't;
it is a mean, wicked lie!"

"Sit down," said Mr. Burrows. "Ellis, did you *see*
him throw it?"

"Yes, sir, I did."

Mr. Burrows turned to Tip. "Edward, come here."

Tip was still standing.

"Say you won't," whispered Bob. "Say you won't
stir a step for the old fellow. If he goes to make you,
we'll see who'll beat."

But the command was repeated, and Tip went
forward, fixing his steady eyes on Mr. Burrows as he
spoke.

"Mr. Burrows, as sure as I live, I did *not* throw that
paper ball."

And yet—poor Tip!—he knew he would not be

believed; he knew his word could not be trusted; he knew he had often stood there and as boldly declared what was *not* true and what had been proved in a few minutes to be false.

No, nobody believed Tip. He had earned, among other things in the school, the name of hardly ever speaking the truth; and now he must suffer for it. So he stood still and received the swift, hard blows of the ruler on his hands; stood without a tear or a promise. Mr. Burrows had not a doubt of his guilt, for had not Ellis Holbrook, whose word was law in the school, said he saw the mischief done? And did not Tip always deny all knowledge of such matters until made to own them?

Still, this time the boy resolutely refused to confess that he had thrown a bit of paper that day and went back to his seat with smarting hands and the stern words of his teacher ringing in his ears.

What a heavy, bitter heart the poor boy carried out from the schoolroom that afternoon; he felt as though he almost hated every scholar there; *quite* hated Ellis Holbrook.

Mr. Burrows, catching a glimpse of his face, said to one of the other teachers, "That boy grows sullen; with all the rest, his good nature was the only good thing which he had about him, and he is losing that."

Tip heard him and felt that it was true. He had been punished many a time before and taken it with the most provoking good humor. But today it was different; today, for the first time in his life, he had received a punishment which he did not deserve; this day of all others, in which he had tried with all his heart to do right.

"Why didn't you hold on, you simpleton?" Bob asked. "Never saw you get up so much pluck in my life. What made you back out and be whipped like a baby?"

"Why didn't *you* own that you threw that plaguey paper ball, and not sit there like a coward and see me take your whipping?"

"I own it, that's a good one! 'Pon honor, Tip, didn't you throw that ball? I thought you did; I was aiming one at Ellis Holbrook's head just then, and I didn't see what was going on behind me. Didn't you throw it, honor bright?"

"No, I didn't; and I'll throw *you* if you say so again."

And Tip turned suddenly in the opposite direction, but Satan still walked with him.

"It's no use," said this evil spirit, speaking out boldly. "It's no use; don't you see it isn't? You might as well give it up first as last; the boys and the teacher, and everyone, think you're nothing in the world but a wicked young scamp, and you never *can* be anything else. You've been humbugging yourself these four weeks, making believe you had a great Friend to help you; why hasn't he helped you today? You've tried your best all day long, and he knows you have; yet you never had such a hard day in your life. If he cares anything at all about you, why didn't he help you today? You asked him to."

Tip sat down on a log by the side of the road and gave himself up for a little to Satan's guidance, and the wicked voice went on:

"Now, you see, you've been cheated. You've tried hard for a whole month to *be* somebody, and no one thinks any more of you than they did before, and never will. Your mother scolds just as much, and your home looks just as dismal, and Kitty is just as hateful, and the respectable boys in the village have nothing to do with you; you might just as well lounge around and have a good time. Nobody expects you to be good, or will let you, when you want to be."

Softly there came another voice knocking at Tip's heart. At first he would not notice it, but it *would* be heard.

"What of all that?" it said. "Suppose nobody cares for you, or helps you here. Jesus died, you know, and he is your friend; you *know* that is not a humbug; you *know* he has heard you when you knelt down and prayed. He has helped you. Then there's heaven, where all the beauty is, and he has promised to take you—yes, *you*—there by and by! Oh, you must not complain because people won't believe that such a bad boy as you have been has grown good so soon. Christ knows about it, so it's all right; just keep on trying, and one of these days folks will see that you mean it; they *will*—God has promised. He has given you a lamp to light you. Why have not you looked at it all this day?"

"Oh!" said Tip, "I can't; I *can't* be a Christian! I have not done right nor felt right today. I almost hate the boys, and Mr. Burrows, too. I don't know what to do."

"Go on home," said Satan. "Let the lamp and these new notions and all *go!* Christ don't care anything about *you;* such a miserable, wicked, storytelling boy as you have been, do you expect him to notice *you?*"

But Tip's hand was in his pocket, resting on his lamp, as he had learned to call it; and the low, sweet voice in his heart was urging him to let its light shine. He drew it out and turned the leaves, and the same dear Helper stopped his eyes at the words "Fear not: for I have redeemed thee, I have called thee by thy name; thou art *mine.*"

Then came hot, thankful tears. Oh, precious words, sinking right into the torn, troubled heart. Christ the Redeemer had called him by his name! He was—yes, he *would be his!* He glanced around. Nobody was to be seen; he was sitting in the hollow at the foot of the hill and under the shade of a low-branching tree. And there he knelt down to pray; and Satan drew himself away, for the spot around that kneeling boy was holy ground. Tip's soul had gained the victory.

8

Freely ye have received, freely give.

WHETHER Tip felt it or not, there were some changes in his home. Mrs. Lewis, though worried and hurried and cross enough, still was not so much so as she had been.

The house was quieter, there was no cradle to rock, there were no baby footsteps to follow and keep out of danger; she had more time for sewing. Yet this very thing, the missing of the clinging arms about her neck, sometimes made her heavy heart vent itself in short, sharp words.

But Tip had astonished the family at home—it didn't require wonderful changes to do it—rather the change which they saw in him seemed wonderful.

The fire which she found ready made in the morning, the full pail of fresh water, the box filled with wood, were all so many drops of honey to the tired mother's heart. The awkward pat of his father's pillow, which Tip now and then gave as he lingered to ask how he was, seemed so new and delightful to that neglected father's heart that he lay on his hard bed and thought of it much all day.

Tip got on better at home than anywhere else; he had not so many temptations. He had been such a lawless, reckless boy that they had all learned to leave him very much to himself, and as not a great deal of his time was spent there, his trials at home were not many. As for Kitty, she did not cease to wonder what had happened to Tip; she perhaps felt the difference more than anyone else, for it had been the delight of his life to tease her.

Now from the time that he gathered his books, with the first sound of the school bell, and hurried up the hill, until he returned at night ready to split wood, hoe in the garden, or do any of the dozen things that he had never been known to do before, he was a never-failing subject of thought and wonderment to her; watching him closely, the only thing she could finally settle on as the cause of the change which she found in him was that he now went every Sabbath morning to the Sabbath school. The mystery must be hidden there. Having decided that matter, Kitty speedily resolved that she would go there herself and see what they did. Many were the kind hearts that had tried to coax her into that same Sabbath school and had failed. But this Saturday afternoon's gazing out of the window with a wonderfully sober face had ended in her exclaiming:

"I say, Mother, I want a needle and thread."

"What do you want of a needle and thread?" asked Mrs. Lewis, stirring away at some gruel in a tin basin and not even glancing up.

"I want to mend my dress; it's torn this way and that and looks awful. I want some green thread, the color of this wide stripe."

Now for a minute the gruel was forgotten, and Mrs. Lewis looked at Kitty in amazement.

"Dear me!" she said at last; "I don't know what will happen next. It can't be possible that you are going to work to mend your own dress without being scolded about it for a week and then made to do it."

"Yes, I am, too; I ain't going to look like a ragbag another hour. And I'm going to wash out my sunbonnet and iron it; then I mean to go over to that Sunday school tomorrow. I ain't heard any singing since I was born, as I know of, and I mean to."

The gruel began to burn, and Mrs. Lewis turned to it again, saying nothing, but thinking a great deal. Once she used to go to Sabbath school herself, when she was Kitty's age; and she didn't have to mend her dress first, either: she used to be dressed freshly and neatly, every Sabbath morning, by her mother's own careful hand.

She poured the gruel into a bowl and then went over to her workbox.

"Here's a needle and thread," she said at last, drawing out a snarl of green thread from the many snarls in her box. "Mend your dress if you want to, and I'll wash out your bonnet for you toward night when I get that vest done."

It was Kitty's turn to be astonished now. She had not expected help from her mother.

Tip lingered in the kitchen on Sabbath morning; he looked neat and clean; he had a fresh, clean shirt, thanks to the washing which his mother had done "toward night." He was all ready for school, yet he waited.

Kitty clattered around, making rather more noise even than usual as she washed up the few poor dishes.

Evidently Tip was thinking about her. The truth was, his lamp had shown him a lesson that morning like this, "Freely ye have received, freely give." He stopped at that verse, reading no farther. What did it mean? Surely it spoke to him. Had not God given, oh, *so* many things to him? Had he not promised to give him heaven for his home? Now, here was the direction: "Freely give." What, and to whom? To God? Surely not. Tip was certain that he had nothing to give to God; nothing but his poor, sinful heart, which he believed the Savior had taken and made clean.

What could he give to anyone? He leaned out of his little window, busy with this thought. Kitty came out to the door and pumped her pan full of water. He looked down on her. There was Kitty; had he anything which he could give her? He shook his head mournfully; not a thing. But wouldn't it be the same if he could help her to get something? What if he could coax her to go to Sunday school; perhaps it would do for her all that it had done for him. And at this moment the unwearied Satan came with his wicked thoughts.

"Kitty would be a pretty-looking object to go to Sabbath school; not a decent thing to wear; everybody would laugh at her and at you; besides, I don't believe she would go if you *did* ask her; she would only make fun of you. Better not try it."

"Oh, Tip Lewis!" said his conscience, "what a miserable coward you are! After all you have promised, you won't risk a laugh for the sake of getting Kitty into the Sabbath school!"

"Yes, I will," said Tip, and he ran downstairs.

And this was why he lingered in the kitchen—not knowing just what to say. Kitty helped him.

"Tip," said she, "I suppose they sing over at that Sunday school; don't they?"

"I guess they do"; and Tip's eyes brightened. "Ever so many of them sing at once, and it sounds great, I tell you. They play the melodeon, too; don't you want to go and hear it?"

"Humph! I don't know. I don't suppose it will be any stupider than staying at home. I get awful sick of that. If I knew the way, maybe I would go."

"Oh, I'll take you," said Tip in a quick, eager way. He wanted to speak before his courage failed.

So Kitty, in her stiff blue sunbonnet and green calico dress, went to Sabbath school. There was no mission class for girls, so Mr. Parker sent her among the gayly dressed little girls in Miss Harley's class; but Mr. Holbrook detained Tip.

"Edward, you intend to come to Sabbath school regularly, don't you?"

"Yes, sir."

"Then I think we must leave your place in the mission seat to be filled by some other boy; and you may come forward to my class."

It is doubtful whether Tip will ever see a prouder or happier moment than that one in which he followed the minister down the long room to his *own* class. But when he saw the seat full of boys, his face grew crimson. At the end of the seat was Ellis Holbrook, the minister's son; the boy who but a few days before had, he believed in his heart, told a wicked story about himself and gained him a severe punishment. He did not feel as though he could sit beside that boy, even in Sabbath school. But Mr. Holbrook waited, and sit down he *must*. Ellis moved along to give him room and disturbed him neither by word nor look during the lesson. But Tip's heart was full of bitterness, and he thought the pleasure of that morning gone. The lesson was of Christ and his death on the cross, and as Tip listened, hard thoughts began to die out; the story was too new; it touched too near his heart not to calm the angry feelings and to interest him wonderfully.

As soon as school was dismissed, Mr. Holbrook turned to him. "What disturbs you today, Edward?"

Tip's face grew red again. "I-I—nothing much, sir."

"Have you and Ellis been having trouble in school?"

"He has been getting *me* into trouble," spoke Tip boldly, finding himself caught.

Mr. Holbrook sat down again. "Can you tell me about it, Edward?"

"He said I threw paper balls, and Mr. Burrows whipped me; and I didn't."

"Are you sure you didn't?"

"Yes, sir."

"Did you say so at the time?"

"Over and over again, but he said he *saw* me."

"Edward, have you always spoken the truth? Is your word to be believed?"

Tip's eyes fell, and his lip quivered. "I've told a great many stories," he said at last, in a low, humble tone; "but this *truly* isn't one. I'm trying to tell the truth after this, and Jesus believes what I have said this time."

"So do I, Edward," answered Mr. Holbrook gently, even tenderly; "Ellis was mistaken. But I see you are angry with him; can't you get over that?"

Tip shook his head. "He got me whipped for nothing, sir."

"Suppose Christ should follow that rule, Edward, and forgive only those who had treated him well; would you be forgiven today?"

This was a new thought to Tip and made him silent. Mr. Holbrook held out his hand for the little red Bible.

"Let me show you what this lamp of yours says about the matter."

And Tip's eyes presently read where the minister's finger pointed, "'If ye forgive not men their trespasses, neither will your Father forgive your trespasses.'"

"'Trespasses' mean sins," explained Mr. Holbrook; then he turned away.

All this time Kitty had been standing waiting—not for Tip; she didn't expect his company—but for the stylish little girls to get fairly started on their way to church, so she could go home without having any of them look at or make fun of her.

Kitty had not been having a very good time; she had the misfortune to fall into the hands of a teacher who thought if she asked the questions in the question book and, if one scholar could not answer, passed on to the next, she had done her duty. So the singing was pretty nearly all Kitty had cared for. God was leaving most of the work for Tip to do, after all. He went over to her now and walked down the road with her. The boys had all gone, as well as the girls, so there was nothing to hinder their walking on quietly together.

"How did you like it, Kitty?" he asked.

"Oh, I didn't think much of it. I sat by the ugliest girl in town, and she made fun of my bonnet and my shoes. I *hate* her."

Tip had a faint notion in his heart that Kitty also needed the verse which had just been given him; but he had other thoughts about her. God's Spirit was at work. Having taken her to Sabbath school—having begun a good work, he wanted it to go on. It was very hard to speak to Kitty; he didn't know what to say; but all the way down the hill there seemed to ring in his ears the message, "Freely ye have received, freely give."

"Kitty," he said at last, "don't you want to be a Christian?"

"I don't know what a Christian is."

"But wouldn't you like to love Jesus?"

"How do *I* know?" replied Kitty shortly. "I don't know anything about Jesus."

"Oh, didn't you hear in the lesson today about how he loves everybody and wants everybody to love him, and how he died so we could?"

"I don't know a thing about the lesson. I counted the buttons on Miss Harley's dress most all the time; they went up and down the front, and up and down the sides, and everywhere."

"Oh, but Kitty, you surely heard the hymn:

Jesus loves me, this I know,
For the Bible tells me so.'"

"Yes," Kitty said; "the hymn was pretty enough, only nobody gave me a book, and I could just hear a word now and then."

Altogether, Tip didn't feel that he had done Kitty a bit of good. But he knew this much: that since he had begun to think about and talk to her, he longed—yes, *longed*—with all his heart to have her come to Christ.

* * *

"Ellis, come here a moment," said Mr. Holbrook, turning toward his study door as the family came in from church. "What is it about this trouble in school with Edward Lewis?"

"No trouble, Father; only Tip threw a paper ball, just as he always *is* doing, and as Mr. Burrows asked me if I knew who threw it, of course I had to tell him, and that made Tip mad. Why? Has he been complaining to you, Father?"

"Ellis, did you see Edward throw paper?"

"Yes, sir."

"Are you positive?"

"Yes—why, that is—I glanced up from my book just in time to see it whiz, and it came from Tip's direction, and his hand was raised, so I supposed of course he threw it. I thought a minute ago that I knew he did."

"But now you would not say positively that some boy near him might not have done it?"

"Why, no, sir—Alex Palmer might have thrown it; but I didn't think of such a thing."

"Well, Ellis, my verdict is that you were mistaken; I don't think Edward told a falsehood this time. I'll tell you why: He is trying to take the Savior for his pattern. I believe he is a Christian. Now, there is one thing which I want you to think of. Edward Lewis, who has never been taught anything good, who has never had anyone to help him, has given his heart to Christ; and my boy, for whom I have prayed with all my soul every day since he was born, has not."

9

Hitherto hath the Lord helped us.

"BOYS," said Mr. Burrows one Monday afternoon, "you may lay aside your books; I want to have a talk with you."

Books were hurriedly gathered and piled in their places, and the boys sat up with folded arms, ready for whatever their teacher had to offer.

Mr. Burrows drew out his armchair from behind the desk and sat down for a chat.

"Who will tell me what an acrostic is?"

Several hands were raised.

"Well, Howard, let us hear what you think about it."

"It's a piece of poetry, sir, where the first letter of every line spells another word."

"Do you mean the first letter alone spells a word?"

The boys laughed, and Howard explained promptly. "No, sir; I mean the first letters of each line taken together form a name."

"Must an acrostic always be written in poetry?"

This question called forth several answers and made a good deal of talk; but it was finally decided that there could be acrostics in prose as well as in rhyme; and Mr. Burrows asked:

"How many understand now what an acrostic is?"

A few more hands were raised, but many of the boys did not understand yet; it must be made plainer.

"Howard," said Mr. Burrows, "come to the board and give us an acrostic on the word 'boy.'"

Howard sprang up. "Must it be a sensible one, sir?"

"Sense or nonsense, just as you please, so as it shows us what an acrostic is."

"I can take my parsing book and give you one, I think, sir."

And Howard came forward and wrote rapidly:

"B   *But you shall hear an odd affair, indeed,*
 O   *Of which all Europe rings from side to side—*"

Then he paused, turning the leaves of his parsing book eagerly.

"I can't find anything in *Y* to finish this up with," he said at last.

"Can't you give us a line from your own brain?"

And at this Howard's eye brightened with fun, and turning to the board after a moment of thought, he dashed off the closing line:

"Y   *You who can finish this may have the job.*"

Then he took his seat amid bursts of laughter from the boys, who all began to understand what an acrostic was.

Ellis Holbrook's hand was up, and his eyes were full of questions.

"Mr. Burrows, why is that called by such a queer name as acrostic?"

His teacher smiled.

"You must study Greek, Ellis. We get it from two words in the Greek, or from one word made up of two

others, which mean 'extreme' or 'beginning,' and
'order.' In an acrostic the beginnings of the lines are
arranged in order. Do you understand how we get
that word now?"

"Yes, sir."

"Well, now, you would all like to know what this
talk is for. I want every boy in school who can write
to bring an acrostic on his own name for his next
composition."

The boys groaned and exclaimed, "They couldn't
do it, they were sure; they couldn't *begin* to do it!"

"Yes, you can," said Mr. Burrows; "I don't give my
scholars any work that they *can't* do. You may quote it,
or make it original, as you please; but I want every one
of you to *try.*"

Johnny Thorpe, the smallest boy in school who
could write, now seemed in trouble and stretched up
his arm to its full length.

"Well, Johnny, what will you have?" asked his
teacher.

"If you please, sir, I don't know what you mean by
'quote.'"

Mr. Burrows laughed pleasantly.

"I must remember, I see, to speak plain English; I
mean you may borrow your essay from a book, or a
dozen books, if you like, so that you don't try to make
us believe the thoughts are your own. You may write
in poetry or not, as you please; but I want each to
choose a subject and stick to it better than Howard
did just now. I have given you something to do that
will keep you hard at work, but you will succeed at
last."

Tip went home in a tumult. What could he do? He
had never written a composition in his life, having
made it a point to run away from school on compo-

sition day; but running away was done with now. It didn't seem possible that he could write anything; certainly not in such a new, queer way as Mr. Burrows wished them to.

Supper and wood splitting were hurried over for that evening, and Tip took his way very early to the seat under the elm tree down by the pond. He wanted to think, to see how he should meet this new trouble; it was a real trouble to him, for he had set out to do just right, and he saw no way of getting out of this duty and thought he saw no way of doing it.

"There is no place on the road so dark but this lamp will light you through, if you give it a chance."

This is what Mr. Holbrook had said when he gave Tip his Bible. And Tip had thought of his words very often, had already proved them true more than once; but he didn't see how it could help him now.

He took it out and slowly turned the leaves; it couldn't write his composition for him, that was certain. But oh, the bright thought that came to Tip just then! Why not find his acrostic in the Bible and write it out? Among so many, *many* verses, he would be sure to find what he wanted. But, then, how very queer it would be for *him,* Tip Lewis, to copy anything from the Bible. What would the boys think? What would Bob Turner say? Still, what else could he do? Besides his spelling book and a worn arithmetic, it was the only book that he had in the world.

"I don't care," he said suddenly, after a few moments of troubled thought. "I guess I ain't ashamed of my Bible—it's the only thing I've got that I needn't be ashamed of—I'll *do* it. The boys have got to know that I've turned over a new leaf; I wish they did; the sooner they know it the better. I say, my lamp shall help me out of this scrape, that's as true as can be; it helps me whenever I give it a chance."

He fumbled in his pocket and drew out an old stump of a pencil; the next thing was a piece of paper; he dived his hand down into another pocket, producing a rusty knife, pieces of string, a chestnut or two, and, finally, a crumpled piece of paper on which Bob Turner had scrawled what he called a likeness of Mr. Burrows and had given to Tip for a keepsake. He spread it out on a flat stone which lay near him and began his work.

A long, slow work it was for Tip. Hours of that day, and the next and the next, every day, until the fading light drove him home, did he sit under the elm tree turning the leaves of his Bible, poring over its contents, writing words carefully now and then on his bit of paper. Remember, it was new work to him.

At last, one evening, the sun went down in the bright red west, the stars shone out in all their twinkling, sparkling glory, the shadows began to fall thick and fast around the old tree, when Tip, with a little sigh of relief, folded the precious piece of paper, laid it carefully away in his Bible, and turned his steps homeward. His acrostic was finished, and into his heart had crept some of the beauty of those precious words, which he had found for the first time. Words they were which would go with him through all his life and sweetly comfort some dark and weary hours.

The schoolbooks were all piled neatly on the desks that Friday afternoon; the shades were dropped to shut out the low afternoon sun, and forty boys were still and expectant. The acrostics lay in a great white heap on Mr. Burrows's desk, not a name written on any of them. Mr. Burrows was to read, and the boys were to have the pleasure of spelling out the names of the owners as he read.

A merry time they had of it that afternoon; some wonderful acrostics were read. Ellis Holbrook had a very clever one, arranged from his lesson in Virgil. Howard Minturn had borrowed from his father's library a copy of Shakespeare and worked hard over his; the boys and their teacher thought it a success.

Even Bob Turner had written; the idea had happened to strike him as a very funny one, and Bob always did everything that he thought funny. He had found three lines in rhyme which just suited him, and by the time the eager boys had spelled out *B O B*—which was the only name the boy saw fit to own—the schoolroom fairly shook with their laughter.

Next to his lay a paper which Tip knew, and his heart beat so loudly when Mr. Burrows took it up that he thought everyone in the room must notice.

The room had now grown quiet, and Mr. Burrows, after opening the paper, announced the title:

"What Jesus Christ Says."

Then he read slowly and reverently, while the wondering scholars spelled out the name.

> "E   *Even the night shall be light about thee.*
> D   *Depart from evil, and do good.*
> W *Whosoever cometh unto me, I will in no wise cast out.*
> A   *A new heart will I give you.*
> R   *Resist the devil, and he will flee from you.*
> D   *Draw nigh to God, and he will draw nigh to thee.*

L   *Lo, I am with you alway.*
E   *Ever follow that which is good.*
W   *Whosoever abideth in him sinneth not.*
I   *I will go before thee, and make the crooked*
     paths straight.
S   *So that we may boldly say, The Lord is my*
     helper."

What a silent and astonished company listened to this reading and spelled the name Edward Lewis!

"Edward," Mr. Burrows said at last, "who found those verses for you?"

"I found them, sir, in my Bible. I've got them all marked!" Speaking eagerly, willing this time to bring proof that he was telling the truth.

Mr. Burrows's voice almost trembled as he answered:

"It is a beautiful collection of some of the most precious verses in the Bible. It was a fine idea; I am very much surprised and pleased. I wish that you, and every scholar of mine, could feel in your hearts the full meaning of those words of Jesus."

* * *

"I can't tonight, Howard," said Ellis Holbrook, in answer to his friend's coaxings to accompany him home; "I've got something else to attend to. Hallo, Tip! Tip Lewis! Hold on a bit, I'm going your way. No, Howard, I'll come up in the morning; I really *can't* tonight."

Tip waited in wondering silence while the boy, whom he counted an enemy, hurried toward him.

Ellis was a bold, prompt boy; when he had anything to say he *said* it; so he came to the point at once.

"See here, Tip, did I blunder the other day, when I

told Mr. Burrows you threw paper? I thought I saw you."

"Yes," said Tip, "you did. I didn't throw a bit of paper that day."

"Well, Father said he thought I was mistaken. I'm sure I supposed I was telling the truth. I'm sorry. I'll say so to Mr. Burrows and the boys, if you like, and let him find out who did it and then was mean enough to see you whipped for it."

Tip struggled a little. "No," he said at last, "let it go; the whipping is done and can't be undone; I don't want to make any more bother about it."

Ellis eyed him curiously.

"You're a queer fellow," he said at last. "I expect you had about the best acrostic this afternoon that can be written."

Tip's heart was throbbing with pleasure as he walked on home after Ellis had left him. For the first time in his life he had earnest, warm, hearty praise from his teacher. Ellis had said, "Father told me he thought I was mistaken." Mr. Holbrook, then, did believe and trust him. Besides, there was another thought which seemed delightful to him. Tip Lewis, the worthless, yes, wicked boy that everybody thought him, had walked down the main street side by side and talking earnestly with Ellis Holbrook, the minister's son.

10

Enter not into the path of the wicked.

KITTY hung on the gate and watched them pass by the long train of high wagons with grated windows, out of which strange animals peered with their great fierce eyes: the two elephants in their scarlet-and-gold blankets; the tiny ponies tossing their shaggy manes; the splendid carriage drawn by eight gayly blanketed, gayly plumed dancing horses, and every seat filled with splendidly dressed men and women; the bright red bandwagon, with the sun glittering over the wonderful brass instruments and turning them into gold. Kitty watched all this; watched, and listened to the loud, full bursts of music, until her heart swelled and bounded. She sprang from the gate and stamped her foot on the ground.

"I wish, oh, I wish I could go!" she almost screamed at last. "I want to; I *want* to; oh, I never wanted to go anywhere so bad in my life."

"I reckon you'll take it out in wanting," said her mother, who had also leaned on the fence and watched the show pass by. "Folks who have to dig as I do, from morning to night, just to get something to eat, don't have any money to spend on circuses."

Kitty shook her head with rage. "I don't go

anywhere," she screamed. "Never! I never went to a circus in my life, and all the boys and girls around here go every year. Tip always goes, always; he manages to slip in. Oh, Tip!" And she opened the gate and went out to him on the sidewalk, a new thought having come to her.

"Can't you do something to get some money, and let me go to the circus with you? Can't you manage some way? Oh, Tip, do! I'll do anything for you, if you only will; I never wanted anything so bad before."

And Tip's face, as he walked toward the village ten minutes after that, was a study, it looked so full of trouble.

Kitty wanted to go to that circus; wanted to go so very much that she had coaxed and begged him in a way that she had never done before. Besides, if the truth be told, Tip wanted to go himself; every time the wind wafted back to him a swell of the distant music, it made his heart fairly jump. It was true, as Kitty had said, he always managed to slip in some way; and the oftener he went, the oftener he wanted to go.

Well, then, what was the matter with Tip? What he had done so many times before, he could surely find a way to do again. Oh yes! But Tip Lewis today was different from any Tip Lewis there had ever been before on circus day. Wasn't he trying to do right? But then, what had circuses to do with that? He tried to think what were his reasons for being troubled! Why did a small voice down in his heart keep telling him that the circus was no place for him now?

Looking at the matter steadily, the only reason Tip knew was that Ellis Holbrook and Howard Minturn never went; their fathers had taught them differently. Ellis, he knew, rather looked down on people who did go; called them low. This had never troubled Tip before, because he had always known himself to be low; but now, wasn't he trying to climb? Didn't respectable people generally think that circuses were bad things?

No, poor Tip, they didn't; there was Mr. Bailey, a rich man—so rich and so respectable that his son wouldn't stoop to lend Tip his spelling book at school—yet Mr. Bailey went to the circus last year and took all his children. So did Mr. Anderson and Mr. Stone, and oh, dozens of others, rich, great men. Well, did good people go? and Tip's thoughts strayed back to Mr. Holbrook, and Mr. Parker and Mr. Minturn, yea, and others, whose voices he had heard on the streets and in stores, condemning the circus.

But then, after all, where was the harm? There was Kitty; how much she wanted to go; if he could manage to take her, how glad she would be! At this point Satan thought there was a chance for him to speak; so he walked along with Tip, talking like this:

"Kitty has never asked you to do anything for her before; you want to help her; you want to get her to go to Sunday school and to read the Bible; now it's your time; if you take her to the circus, very likely she will do what you want her to."

This was a little too absurd, even for Tip, who wanted to believe it all so badly; but whoever heard of taking anyone to a circus in order to get them to love Jesus! Tip knew altogether too well for his comfort that day that Mr. Holbrook's example was the safe one. At last he drew a little sigh of relief; he needn't think about it anymore, for he had no money; he had never owned fifty cents at one time in his life; so the question, after all, would settle itself.

No, it wouldn't. Mr. Dewey stood in the door of his market, looking up and down the street.

"Halloa, Tip!" he called as Tip turned the corner; "you're the boy I must have been looking for, I guess. If you'll carry home packages for me for an hour, and not steal one of them, I'll give you two tickets for the circus."

Tip's cheeks glowed at the word 'steal,' and he came near telling Mr. Dewey to carry his own packages if he were afraid to trust him.

But then, those two tickets! Here was a chance for Kitty; the conflict commenced again.

A whole hour in which to decide it, for Tip meant to do the work anyway. Up and down the streets, stopping at this house and that with his parcels, back again to the market for more, all the time in a whirl of thought; the question was almost decided when the two green tickets were placed in his hand; it closed over them eagerly; he hurried toward home.

Toward home led him past the brick hotel. In the barroom sat some of the circus men; he knew them by their heavy beards which almost covered their faces; knew them also because he knew every man in town, just who were strangers and who were not. Well, these circus men were very busy drinking brandy and playing cards. Tip stopped and looked in at them; and, ignorant boy as he was, the thought that good, re-spectable people would go to see and hear such men as these seemed very strange. It couldn't be right, could it? How was it? A great many nice people must have blundered terribly if it were wrong; and, on the other hand, if it were not wrong, how did the minister happen to be so afraid of these things? Why did he himself have so many queer feelings about the matter?

What a trouble he was in! If only he could find somebody or something that would decide it for him! Long before this, he had walked away from the hotel;

now he had crossed the bridge, gone around behind the mill, and was very near his seat under the elm. Down he sat when he came to it, still holding fast the two green tickets, but with the other hand diving down in his pocket for the little Bible. That was getting to be a habit with him, to hunt for this lamp of his whenever he was in darkness; he turned the leaves now with a perplexed face; if he only knew where to turn for help!

"Let me see," he said. "Where was that verse that I learned for the Sunday school concert? I liked the sound of that; it was somewhere in this book full of short, queer verses. I can find it; yes, I see it. 'For the Lord shall be thy confidence, and shall keep thy foot from being taken.'"

It didn't seem to help him; he shook his head slowly, still glancing on over the verses, until suddenly his listless look vanished, and he read aloud: "'Enter not into the path of the wicked, and go not in the way of evil men. Avoid it, pass not by it, turn from it, and pass away.'

"That means them," said Tip, "and me. They're wicked men, that's certain; they were drinking and gambling; swearing, too, I guess; and this verse reads about them just as plain as day. It says, 'Don't go near them'; says it over and over again; and I'll mind it, I will. I'll take these tickets right back to Mr. Dewey, so they won't be here to put me in mind of going."

No sooner said than done; he turned around and fairly galloped up the hill, around the corner, and landed nearly breathless at the market.

"Here, Mr. Dewey," he said promptly. "I've brought back your tickets; I don't want 'em this time."

"What's up now?" asked Mr. Dewey, coming out

from behind his desk and eyeing the panting boy curiously. "Won't the tickets pass?"

"Not if they wait till I pass 'em," answered Tip in his prompt, saucy way; "I ain't going to the circus, not an *inch,*" he added, as if to assure himself that he meant it.

"But why not?"

"Oh, I've got reasons."

"Well, now, Tip," said Mr. Dewey, "that's really astonishing; suppose you give us a few of your reasons; we don't know what to make of this."

Tip didn't know what to say; he hesitated and thought, and finally doing the best thing he *could,* spoke out boldly.

"I've made up my mind that I won't go to any more circuses, *ever!* I don't believe in 'em as much as I did."

That wasn't it, yet he had not owned his Master in the answer. Neither was Mr. Dewey satisfied.

"But, Tip, give us the *reasons;* this is such a sudden change, you know."

"Well," said Tip, "I've been reading about them just now."

"About whom?"

"Why, them circus fellows. They're up here at the tavern; they're drinking and fighting, and I don't know what; and I guess, by the looks of things, they're pretty wicked. The book I was reading said, Don't go near wicked men, turn around and go the other way; and I *mean* to." And, with this, Tip whisked out of the house and around the corner.

Mr. Dewey shrugged his shoulders.

"The world turns around, sure enough," he said at last.

"How do you know that?" and Mr. Minturn set his market basket on the step and fanned himself with his hat. "I'm my own boy today, you see; give me something for my dinner. How did you find out that the world turned around?"

"Why, Tip Lewis has taken to preaching against circuses. Will you have a roast today, Mr. Minturn? I gave him a ticket, and he just rushed in with it and informed us he wasn't going to circuses anymore, because the Bible says they are wicked fellows; what do you think of that?"

"Humph!" said Mr. Minturn. "The Bible says it would be better for a man, sometimes, if a millstone were about his neck, and he were in the bottom of the sea. I'd look out for that, if I were you. Hurry up with your meat; I ought to be at the store."

Tip went home to Kitty. She still swung on the gate; at least she was there when he came up.

"Oh, Tip!" she said, "are you going to take me? Oh, Tip, *do.* I never asked you for anything before."

Tip walked slowly up the yard with his hands in his pockets, troubled—not knowing what to say, or how to say it. At last he stopped and wheeled about. "Kitty, I can't; I can't go. I could get tickets if I dared, but I don't mean to go anymore; they're bad, wicked men, and I'm trying to be—"

But Kitty twitched herself away from him and wouldn't hear any more.

"Do go off!" she said. "You're a mean, ugly, hateful boy. I'm sorry you got so awful good, if you can't do that little much for me. Go away, and let me alone."

Even in his sore trouble, a little flash of joy shot through Tip's heart. He *was* different, then. Kitty had noticed it; she knew he was trying to be different. There *must* be a little bit of change in him.

11

Avoid it, pass not by it, turn from it, and pass away.

OVER and over in his mind did Tip repeat this verse; it seemed to sound all around him and mixed up with everything he did. And yet he went out of the house that evening and turned straight down the street in the direction leading to the tented circus grounds. Walking along slowly, talking to himself.

"It won't do any harm just to listen to the music. I don't mean to go in, of course I don't. Suppose I'd do *that,* after all I said to Kitty! Besides, I couldn't if I would. I haven't got any ticket. I'm just going to walk down that way to see if there's lots of folks going and if the music sounds nice."

"Avoid it, pass not by it." Oh yes, Tip knew; he heard the voice, yet on he went, beginning to walk swiftly, only saying in answer, "I ain't going in; I couldn't, if I wanted to; and I don't want to."

By and by he came within sight of the tents and within sound of the music, which, to his untaught ears, was wonderfully beautiful; came up even to the very door of the large tent, bewitched to go just a step nearer, though he didn't mean to go in, not he.

Yes, the people were crowding in. Mr. Douglass stood by the door. Tip knew him very well; that is, he knew he lived in a large house and had plenty of money; and he knew when the men were trying to raise any money, someone was sure to say, "Go to Mr. Douglass; he's always ready to give."

Everybody liked Mr. Douglass. He turned around now from looking down the road and looked down at Tip.

"Well, Tip," he said, "going to the circus?"

Tip shook his head.

"What's the matter—no money? Pity to get so near and not go in; isn't it, pet?"

This last, to the dainty little girl whose hand he held.

"Yes," she answered with a happy smile. "Papa, why don't Mamma come?"

"Oh, she'll be along soon. Here, sir," to the door-keeper, handing him twenty-five cents, "let this raga-muffin in. In with you, Tip, and practice standing on your head for a month to come."

It was all done in a hurry; the doorkeeper stepped aside, the crowd jostled and pushed against him, the music burst forth in a new loud swell. A moment more, and Tip stood in the brightly lighted room, staring eagerly around him: there was enough to see, the seats were filling rapidly with gayly dressed ladies and gentlemen. He knew them, many of them, had seen them on the streets often and often; had seen some of them in Sabbath school, seated before their classes.

Tip was speedily giving himself up to enjoyment; hushing the small voice in his heart. One of the nicest men in town had let him in; yes, and there he was now with his wife and little girl; Mrs. Douglass was not only a teacher in the Sabbath school, but a member of the church. If she could go to the circus, why couldn't he? So Tip reasoned, and nobody told him that his lamp said, "Every one of us shall give account of *himself* to God."

Presently, the wonderful little shaggy ponies trotted out; and back behind the curtains was one of the riders; he got a peep of her every now and then, in her splendid dress; he knew she would be out pretty soon, and then she would ride.

Oh, that music! How it rolled around the ring. Tip was too busy looking and listening to keep out of people's way; he stepped back, still jostled by the crowd who were pouring in, and stepped directly in front of a man who was trying to make his way through the crowd around the entrance. Tip knew him in an instant; he was one of the circus men, the one with the ugly face that he had noticed in the morning; it was ugly still and red with liquor. He turned a pair of fiery eyes on Tip, and a dreadful oath fell from his lips as he swung him angrily out of his way.

Oh, Tip Lewis! No wonder your heart fairly stops its beating for an instant, then bounds on with rapid throbs. Only a few days ago you listened to the story of a bleeding, dying Savior; bleeding and dying for you; and you promised with honest tears that for this you would love and serve and honor him forever. And yet, tonight, here you are, watching the tricks of men who can speak that sacred name in such a way that it will make even you, who are used to this, shudder and turn cold. "In the name of the Savior whom you love, what do you here?"

It was to Tip as if Christ himself had asked that question. He turned suddenly and, with both hands pressed to his ears, fairly fought his way through the crowd.

"Let me out! Let me go!" He fairly shrieked the words at the astonished doorkeeper, who stood aside to let him pass. Up the hill with swift, eager steps he ran, trying still to shut out the ring of that awful oath. The sound of that hateful voice, speaking the name which had so lately become to him the one dear and precious name in earth or heaven. On, on, up the hill, and then down on the other side, stopping finally at the great tree under the hill, just across the pond. Stopping and sitting down, he tried to think. What had he done? He had been warned, he had been tempted, and he had *fallen*. It didn't help him now to think that good men and women were there. Perhaps God had not so plainly shown them the wrong. Perhaps they had never found that verse: "Avoid it, pass not by it." Perhaps—oh, *anything*—it was nothing to him now. This much was certain: he had done wrong. Such a heavy, *heavy* heart as Tip had tonight. What *should* he do? What would Kitty say, if she found it out? Oh, what would Mr. Dewey think, or Mr. Holbrook? And then above all else came the thought, What could Jesus, looking down on him now from heaven, what could *he* think of him? This thought brought the bitter tears, but it brought him also on his knees, and he said:

"Oh, Jesus Christ, in spite of it all, you *know* I love you; won't you forgive me and let me try again?" Long he knelt there, trying to get close to Christ, and his Savior did not leave him alone. It was only yesterday he had learned the verse, and it came to him softly now: " 'Thou art a God ready to pardon, gracious and merciful, slow to anger, and of great kindness.' "

In his sore trouble, Tip's lamp had not failed him.

12

⊶ ═✠═ ⊷

He honoureth them that fear the Lord.

SLOWLY but surely, as the late autumn days came on, Tip was growing into a better place in the school-room, in the opinion of his teachers and his school-mates. In Mr. Burrows's school, ten was the perfect mark, and X was the very lowest grade a boy could reach. It had once been an everyday joke with Tip that being X must be perfect, because it said in the spelling book that X was ten.

But it had been a good many days since Tip had said, "X"; the boys had ceased to be amazed when he answered, "Ten," in prompt, proud tone.

They were growing, many of them, to be surprised and sorry for him when, in his days of failures, he answered with drooped eyes and very red, ashamed face, "Seven," or it might be, "Six."

Though he was still anything but a good reader, no one could fail to see that he blundered less and less every day, and Mr. Burrows was growing patient with his blunders, growing helpful in his troubles.

The boys saw him working hard over his spelling book, and few of them now had the meanness to laugh when a word passed him.

Mr. Burrows's tones were not so harsh to him as

they used to be; and nowadays when he was accused of breaking rules, instead of being called up and unhesitatingly punished, his teacher, who grew every day less and less sure that he was at the bottom of all the mischief done, always gave him a chance to speak for himself and was learning to believe him.

Oh yes! things were different and were all the time growing more so. Bob Turner saw this plainly; he began to find Tip a very stupid companion and stayed away from school more afternoons than ever.

But poor Tip noticed the change less—yes, much less than any of the others. You don't know how hard it was for him. Do you think Satan was willing to leave him and let him grow quietly into a good boy? Not a bit of it. You see, he had been born bubbling over with fun and frolic; he had never learned to have them come in at the right place or the right time.

Sometimes he felt willing to give up all trying to do right for the sake of having a grand frolic just when and where he wanted it—no matter what might be going on just then. Sometimes when he failed, he felt fierce and sullen, and told himself it was all humbug, this trying to be good. Sometimes he felt so utterly sad and discouraged that it seemed to him he never could try again; yet through it all he *did* try heartily.

His arithmetic was the hardest. He was still in the dunce class—so the boys called it, because it was made up of the drones from several classes and was constantly being put back to addition.

It was a sharp winter's morning. No more make-believe winter for a while—the snow lay white and crisp on the ground, and the frosty air stung every nose and every finger it could reach.

Tip's study, at the foot of the hill under the elm, had been quite broken up, and he found it very hard to study at home—especially this morning. His father's cough had been bad all night, and this made his mother troubled and cross.

Kitty, these days, seemed trying to see just how cross and disagreeable she could be, and the kitchen—at best, a dismal place—was just now at the worst. The wet wood in the stove sizzled and stewed and made a smoke; and in the midst of Tip's fifth trial on an example which was puzzling him terribly, he was called on to split some kindling.

"This instant—I won't wait a minute!" Kitty said in a provokingly commanding tone; and Tip went at it sullenly, saying, with every spiteful drive of his ax through the pine board which he had picked up, "It's no use; I *can't* do that sum, and I ain't going to try. I don't know anything and never will. I've done it over fifty times and twisted it every way I can think of. There's no sense to it, anyway—sixteen sheep *stood him in* two dollars apiece. What does that mean, I'd like to know? He had forty sheep and twenty-five cows. I know it all by heart; but I can't do it, and that's the whole of it. I wish his sheep had choked to death and his old cows run away before I ever heard of them. I'll go over it just once more." (Tip was back by the kitchen window now, with his slate and book.) "Let's see, twenty-five cows at thirty-four dollars apiece"—and he worked away in nervous haste, until he came to "stood him in." If he only *could* find out what that meant, he felt sure he could do it. If he had something to help him; but he hadn't. There would be no time after he went to school before the class was called.

Just then he thought of his father; he used to be a carpenter before he was sick, and he used to make a great many figures sometimes on smooth boards. Tip remembered it was just possible that he might know something about the sum; suppose he should ask him?

He started up suddenly and went toward the bedroom door.

"Father," he said softly, "can't you tell me what 'stood him in' means?"

The sick man turned himself on his pillow and looked wonderingly at Tip.

"What do you mean?" he asked at last.

"Why," said Tip in a despairing tone, "it says 'stood him in' in the arithmetic—the sheep stood him in two dollars apiece, and I don't see any sense to it."

"Oh!" said Mr. Lewis, "I see what you mean." Then he went back to his long-ago-deserted carpenter's shop.

"Why, Tip, if I had ten pounds of nails and they were worth eight cents a pound, they would stand me just so much—that is, they would be worth that to me, and if I should sell them I'd get so much for them. Don't you see?"

Light began to dawn on Tip's mind.

"Then it means," he said, "that the man didn't see his sixteen sheep; he just counted them worth two dollars apiece. Yes, I see; if that's it, I'll try it." And he rushed to his work again.

And Tip will never forget the eagerness with which he presently turned to the answer in his arithmetic, and from that back to the one on the slate—nor the way in which the blood bounded through his veins when he found that they agreed perfectly.

"It's exactly it," he called out to his father in a hearty, grateful voice. "I've got it, and I've been at work on it this whole morning."

Ellis Holbrook, about that time, conquered a most

puzzling example in algebra; but he felt not prouder than did Tip.

"Thomas," said Mr. Burrows to the head boy in Tip's arithmetic class, "you may take the twenty-third example to the board."

"Can't do it," answered Thomas promptly.

"Henry may do it then."

"I couldn't get it either," was Henry's answer. So on down the class; Tip's heart meantime beating eagerly, for the twenty-third example was about his troublesome, but by this time very much beloved, sheep.

"Robert?" said Mr. Burrows, more for form's sake than because he had the slightest doubt about Robert's reply.

"My!" said Bob Turner good-naturedly, "I can't do it."

Tip sat next, and something in his face made Mr. Burrows put the question to him, though he had nearly resolved to waste no more time in the matter.

"Can you do this, Edward?"

"Yes, sir," said Tip promptly and proudly; "I can."

And no nobler figures or firmer lines did chalk ever make on a blackboard than were made while that troublesome example was being done.

He was roused from his flutter of satisfaction by hearing Mr. Burrows's voice.

"Do you know anything about the lesson, *any* of you?"

"I'm sure *I* don't," answered Bob, still good-naturedly.

Mr. Burrows was growing utterly out of patience; this same scene had been acted too often to be endured longer. He turned back to the first pages in the book.

"Very well," he said at last; "you may take the first page in addition, tomorrow morning, and we'll see if you can be made to know anything about that."

Tip's hopes fell; his heart was as heavy as lead. Not one of the others cared; they were used to it; so indeed was he, only now he was trying, he did so long to go on; just when he was working *so* hard, to be put away back to the beginning again made him feel utterly disgraced.

"Wait a minute, Tip." Mr. Burrows's eye fell first on him, then on the neatly and correctly worked example; then he turned and asked, "Charlie Wilcox, on what page is your arithmetic lesson for tomorrow?"

"We commence multiplication, sir," answered Charlie, a bright little boy who belonged to a bright class that did not idle over any pages in their work.

"Edward," said Mr. Burrows, turning back to Tip, "you have done well today; you mean to study after this, I think; I have been watching you for some time. The third arithmetic class take the first page in multiplication for their next lesson, tomorrow; you may take your place in that class and remain there as long as you can keep up with it."

Now Tip was too much astonished to speak or move; his wildest dreams had not taken in promotion, at least not for a long, *long* time.

Bob Turner leaned over and looked at him in actual sober wonder that Tip was to be in a higher class.

Not a word did Tip say. He did not even raise his eyes to his teacher's face; and that teacher had not the least idea how the boy before him felt. He did not know how Tip's heart was throbbing, nor how he was saying over and over to himself, "Things are different; they're surely different." He did not know how those few words of his, spoken that winter morning, were going to help make the boy a man.

It was that very morning, standing in that room before the blackboard, with his toe on the third crack from the wall, that Tip resolved to have an education.

13

*The rich and poor meet together:
the Lord is the maker of them all.*

THE BOYS gathered around the stove before school
and talked. The boys—not all of them, by any means.
Only that small, select number who were above and led
all the rest. Tip wandered outside of the circle, feeling
very forlorn; he didn't belong anywhere these days. Bob
and his friends had very nearly deserted him—there
was scarcely any of their fun in which he had time or
desire to join; and the other cliques in school had never
noticed him; so he stood outside and wondered what
he should do with himself. Howard Minturn wheeled
suddenly away from the boys and called to him.

"Tip, see here."

And Tip went there.

"What do you want?" he asked crossly; for, some
way, he felt out of sorts with that company of finely
dressed boys around the stove.

"Want you to come over tonight. It's my birthday,
you know, and some of the boys are coming to take
tea and spend the evening. Can you come?"

Tip's wide-open eyes spoke his astonishment.
"What do you want of me?" he asked at last, speaking
boldly just what he thought.

"Why, I want you to come and help have a nice time," returned Howard with great kindness but just a little condescension in his tone.

Tip heard it, and his bitterness showed itself a little. "It's a new streak you've got, ain't it?" he said, still speaking crossly. "You've had lots of birthdays, and this is the first one *I've* heard of."

"Oh, well!" said Howard proudly, flushing as he spoke; "if you don't want to come, why—"

Mr. Burrows's hand was laid on Howard's arm. "Don't spoil a good, noble thing, my boy; it is all new to Edward; *urge* him."

Mr. Burrows spoke low, so no one else could hear him, and turned away.

At recess Howard sought out Tip.

"I honestly hope you'll come tonight, Tip, for you're a good fellow to play games with, and the boys would all like to have you."

Tip had quarreled with his ill humor, and it had vanished.

"I'll come!" he said in a cheery tone; "only I'll look like a big ragbag by the side of *you* fellows."

"Never mind," said Howard, turning to join the boys, *"you* come."

Why had Howard Minturn invited him to the grand birthday party? This was the question that puzzled Tip. Had he known the reason, it would have been like this: Mr. Minturn had never quite lost sight of Tip since the circus. He wanted to help him; wanted to do it through his son—only he wanted the son to think that he did it himself. Knowing Howard pretty well, he said, when they were seated at breakfast that morning:

"I've just been reading about a real hero."

Howard longed to be a hero; he looked up eagerly.

"Who was he, Father? What did he do?"

"He was a rich young man, and he had the courage to take for his friend a poor fellow who hadn't two cents to his name. To pay him, the time came when he was proud to be noticed by the great man who was once so low."

This thought was still in Howard's mind when he walked with Ellis to school. So when Ellis said, "There goes Tip Lewis; Father thinks we boys ought to notice him; he is trying real hard nowadays to behave himself, you know," it was easy for Howard to mingle Tip in with his thoughts.

"Ellis," he said after a moment's silence, "suppose I invite him to come to our house tonight? He's a splendid good fellow to have a game; never gets mad, you know."

"S'pose he'd come?" asked Ellis.

"Yes, of course; jump at the chance. *I'll do it.* Our boys will think it odd, I suppose; but I guess I have courage enough to do as I please."

And Howard drew himself up proudly and thought of his father's hero.

So this was why Tip was invited to the birthday gathering at the grand house on the hill.

Mrs. Lewis sewed that afternoon on his jacket, mending it up more neatly than ever before. She had said very little about this invitation, but she couldn't help feeling proud and gratified over it. It was certainly a wonderful jump for Tip, from mingling with the worst and lowest boys in town, to find himself taking a long stride and reaching the very top. So Mrs. Lewis sewed, and Kitty, as she sat watching the needle fly back and forth, spoke her thoughts.

"All of the boys down to Mr. Burrows's school wear white collars on their jackets."

"Well," answered her mother snappishly, "what's that to me? S'posing they wear white Etons jackets? I could get him one just as easy as t'other."

It was a sore subject with Mrs. Lewis. From her very heart she wished she could dress Tip in broadcloth today, just as fine as that which Howard Minturn himself wore, and a collar so white and shiny that it would fairly dazzle the eyes of the others to look upon it; but, since she was so powerless to do what she would, it made her cross.

The bedroom door was open, and Tip's father heard. By and by, when his cough was quieter, he called, "Kitty!" and the little girl went in to him. "Is the jacket fixed, Kitty?"

"Yes."

"Does it look nice?"

"Some."

"Would you like to find a collar for Tip to wear?"

"Well enough," said Kitty wonderingly.

"Well, now, I've got two or three that I don't wear anymore, and never shall, I guess" (this last spoken sadly); "s'pose you take one of 'em—they're in that square box under the table—and see if you can't sew it on the jacket and make it look like what the other boys wear? Now, you try what you can do, just to see what Tip will say."

Kitty went slowly over to the box. This was new work for her, but her father was very pale today, and those sadly spoken words, "and never shall, I guess," had quieted her; so she made no answer, but drew out one of the collars. It looked nice and white, and shone, too. Mrs. Lewis had done it up late one night, with tears in her eyes, because she could not hope that it would be worn again.

"What are you doing with that?" she asked sharply, as Kitty appeared from the bedroom.

"Father wants Tip to wear it," answered Kitty.

"I'll lend it to him," spoke the sick man; "we want him to look as decent as we can today, you know."

Mrs. Lewis said no more, but it seemed to her like giving up one more hope of her husband's life.

Tip came down from the garret with neatly brushed hair and dressed in his clean shirt, nicely mended jacket, and the shiny collar. It was wonderful what a difference that collar made; he didn't look like the same boy.

"Kitty," he said, his face all aglow with pleasure, "where *did* I get a collar?"

"It's Father's; he said wear it," answered Kitty.

"And how did it get on my jacket?"

"Jumped on, likely."

Kitty spoke in a short, half-provoked tone; she was so unused to doing a kind thing that she really felt half-ashamed of it.

"Well," said Tip, smiling all over his face, "if that's so, it's the best jump it ever took, and I thank it from the bottom of my heart." Then he carried his bright, good-natured face out of the little house in the hollow and went toward the great house on the hill.

14

Every idle word that men shall speak, they shall
give account thereof in the day of judgment.

HOWARD Minturn was a king among the schoolboys; so, though some of them nudged each other and
laughed a little when Tip swung open the iron gate
and appeared in Mr. Minturn's grounds, the most of
them, seeing how quickly Howard sprang forward and
how heartily he greeted the newcomer, did the same.
Howard was his father over again; if he did a thing at
all he did it well. Every moment of that afternoon was
enjoyed as only boys know how to enjoy holidays; the
whole round of winter fun was gone through with—
coasting, snowballing, building forts, rolling in the
snow—each had their turn.

Tip was not one whit behind the rest in all these
matters, and if ever a boy enjoyed an afternoon, he did
that one. The sun had set in its clear, cold beauty, and
the sharp winter night was coming down; the boys
stood at the foot of the hill waiting for Ellis and his
sled, which were at the top; they came at last, shooting
down the glassy surface.

"Hurry up," called out Howard as he spun along;
"what the mischief became of you? We thought you
had gone to hunt up Sir John Franklin and crew."

"Hurry down, I should say you meant," answered Ellis, guiding his sled skillfully around the curve and springing to his feet. "I waited for the rest of you; thought you were coming back."

"No," said Howard, "we just *ain't;* we appointed a committee to find out how many were frozen up altogether entirely; and found that every single one of us were; so we're going in to the library fire to get thawed out by teatime."

"All right," said Ellis, shouldering his skates; "Howard, where's your skates?"

"Oh, bother! They're at the top of that awful hill; never mind, you walk on slowly, and I'll run back and get them."

The boys obeyed, and Ellis Holbrook was just swinging open the little gate that led to Mr. Minturn's grounds, when Howard called, as he ran down the hill, "Hold on! Don't go that way, it will lead you right through the deepest snow there is; take the big gate." And by the time he reached them, panting and breathless, they were at the big gate.

"This is jolly," said Will Bailey, throwing himself into a great armchair before the glowing fire. "My! I believe I'm a snowball."

"You'd have been an icicle if you had gone the way Ellis was leading you; why, the snow is *so* high," said Howard, raising his hand almost on a level with his head.

Ellis laughed. "I'm sure I thought I was going right," he said. "I must have been thinking of yesterday's lesson in Sunday school: 'Enter ye in at the strait gate.'"

"Ho," said Will Bailey, "for that matter, one gate is as straight as the other."

"You don't understand the Bible, my boy," said

Howard, laying his hand on Will's shoulder with a provoking little pat, "or you'd know that strait means narrow."

"I'll bet a dollar that you were no wiser yourself until Father explained the verse yesterday," said Ellis, laughing.

Tip, meantime, stood apart, flushed and silent; he knew about the Sunday lesson and remembered the solemn talk which Mr. Holbrook gave them; and remembered how he urged them, while they were young, to enter into that strait gate; he felt shocked and troubled at the sound of Ellis's careless words.

"I know one thing," he said abruptly.

"Do you?" said Will Bailey in a mocking tone. "That's very strange!" Will felt above Tip and took care to let him know it.

Ellis turned a quick, indignant glance on him, then spoke to Tip in a kind and interested tone: "What were you going to say, Tip?"

"That if I were the minister's son, I wouldn't make fun of the Bible."

Ellis's face was crimson in an instant. "What do you mean by that?" he asked haughtily.

"Just what I say," was Tip's cool reply.

"Do you pretend to say that *I* make fun of the Bible?"

"Humph! Didn't I hear you?"

"No!" said Ellis in a heat, "you *didn't;* and I'd thank you not to say so neither."

"Well, now," said Tip, "I'll leave it to any boy here if you didn't. When a fellow takes a thing in the Bible and twists it around and makes believe it means some little silly thing that it don't mean at all, I call that making fun."

"Poh?" said Howard, coming to the rescue of his

friend. "What a fuss you're making about nothing. You're getting wise, aren't you, Tip? Ellis was only saying that verse in fun, just as lots of people do. I've heard good men quote the Bible and laugh over it."

"Can't help that," said Tip boldly; "I say it's wicked, and Ellis Holbrook's father says so, too. I heard him tell Will Bailey once that folks ought to be very careful how they said things that were in the Bible."

"Did he tell you to go around preaching for him through the week? How much does he pay you for your services? Come, let's hear."

This was said in Will Bailey's most disagreeable tone. Before Tip had time to answer, Ellis spoke again:

"Well, I don't pretend to be as good as some people are, but I really can't see any awful wickedness in anything that I've said tonight."

"Neither can anybody else, except Tip," said Will, "and he's good, you know; he never does anything wrong, except to tell lies and swear, or some little matters."

Ellis was an honest boy. "No," he said gravely, "there is no use in saying what isn't true for the sake of helping my side along. Tip don't do either of those things nowadays, I believe; but I'm sure I don't thank him for his good opinion of me."

Howard was glad at this moment to hear the tea bell peal through the house, for the boys were growing cross. Most of them had been so astonished at the bold stand which Tip had taken that they said nothing, only gathered round and waited to see what would come next. Howard sprang up—"There's something I, for one, am ready for; come, boys"—and he led the way to the dining room. Oh, that dining room, with its bright lights and splendid table, was such a wonderful sight to Tip! It was a very nice birthday supper—

plates of warm biscuit, platters of cold chicken, dishes of beautiful honey, silver cake baskets filled with heavily frosted cake. Tip, for one, had never seen such a sight in his life before, and he was so bewildered with the dazzle and glitter that he didn't know which way to turn.

"Howard," said Mrs. Minturn, turning to her son after she had welcomed his friends, "do you want your father to take the head of the table, or would you and the boys prefer having the room to yourselves?"

"No, *ma'am*," answered Howard with energy; "we want you and Father *both*. I guess I want *you* to my party, whoever else I have."

Tip watched the bright light on Howard's face with surprise—how much he seemed to love his mother, and how much she loved him—how queer it was. The supper was a great success; the boys forgot their excitement and ill humor, and enjoyed everything.

It was almost nine o'clock, the hour when it was generally understood that the party was to break up. The boys had been very merry all the evening; the discussion which had taken place just before tea seemed to have been forgotten, save by Ellis, who, genial and hearty enough with the others, was cold and haughty to Tip. Still they kept apart, and the fun had gone on famously. There was a sudden lull in the uproar when Mr. Minturn opened the door.

"Are the walls left?" he asked, coming forward.

"The *walls?*" said Ellis inquiringly; "why, sir, did you expect to miss them?"

"Well, I had some such fears, but I see they're all right. What are you up to?"

"Ellis was telling a story, that's what we were laughing at when you came in," said Howard. "Go on El—never mind Father; he likes to hear stories."

"No," said Ellis, blushing crimson, "I think I'll be excused."

"Go ahead," said Mr. Minturn, "I'm very fond of stories."

"I was only telling, sir, how Joe Barnes talked to his father when I was down there this morning."

"Yes, and Father, you'd be perfectly astonished to hear him," chimed in Howard. "I never heard a fellow go on so in my life; he makes fun of every single thing his father says."

"Do you think there is anything very surprising in that?" asked Mr. Minturn coolly.

"Surprising! I guess you'd think so. Why, when his father is talking to him real soberly, he mimics him and laughs right in his face."

"But I shouldn't suppose you would think there was anything strange about that."

The boys looked puzzled. "Why, Mr. Minturn!" said Ellis, "wouldn't you think it strange if Howard should do so?"

"Well, no; I don't know as I should have any reason to be astonished."

Howard looked not only surprised, but very much hurt. "I'm sure, Father," he said in a voice which trembled a little, "I didn't know I was so rude to you as all that."

"No," said Mr. Minturn, "you never have been, but I rather expect you to commence. I shall have no reason to be surprised if you and Ellis and Will Bailey, and a host of others, all go to making fun of what your fathers say to you after this."

The boys seemed perfectly astonished. "*I*, for one," said Ellis Holbrook proudly, "think too much of *my* father to be in any such danger."

"You *do?*" said Mr. Minturn; "well, now, I *am*

amazed. I supposed you would be the very worst one."

Howard left the table and came over to where his father had seated himself.

"Father, what *do* you mean?" he asked in an earnest, anxious tone.

"Why, I mean," said his father, "that I was in that room over there just before tea, and I heard the discussion which came up between you boys, and I came to the conclusion that boys who thought it such a little matter to make fun of solemn words which God has said to them need not be expected to show much respect for what their father or anybody else said."

A perfect stillness settled over the boys at these words, and not only Ellis Holbrook's cheeks but his whole face glowed.

Howard came to the rescue at last, very stammeringly, "But, Father—I don't think—do you think—I mean—well, sir, you know Ellis and the rest of us didn't mean to make fun of what God said. Don't you think that makes a difference?"

"I don't know, I'm sure. How do you know that Joe Barnes means to make fun of what his father says?"

"He acts like it," Howard said.

"Exactly; and so do you, every one of you, except Tip. I don't say, boys, that you are all going to be disrespectful to your elders after this; I only say I don't see why your earthly friends should expect more reverence from you than you give to God."

Boys and man were all silent for a little after that, until Mr. Minturn broke the stillness by repeating reverently, "'Enter ye in at the strait gate.' I guess you all know what that means. I would like to know whether there is a boy here who thinks he has entered in at that gate."

How still the room was while he waited for his answer! Tip could feel his heart throb—throb—with loud, distinct beats; twice he tried to break the silence and couldn't. At last he found voice. "I do, sir."

Mr. Minturn turned quickly. "What makes you think so, Tip?"

"Because I love Jesus, and I'm trying to do what he says."

Mr. Minturn's voice trembled a little. "God bless you, my boy; try to get all the rest to go through the same gate."

The town clock struck the hour, nine o'clock. The boys made a move to separate. Tip took his cap and walked out alone in the cold, clear starlight. He felt quiet and strong. It was done at last; he had taken his stand before the boys—had "shown his colors."

They all knew now that he was trying hard and who was helping him. Things must surely be different after this, forever.

15

*And all things, whatsoever ye shall ask in prayer,
believing, ye shall receive.*

MEANTIME, was Kitty forgotten? Not a bit of it. If ever a boy prayed for anyone, Tip prayed for her. His very soul was in it; yet thus far his prayers seemed to have been in vain. The lesson one Sabbath morning was on "God's answers to prayer." Tip listened closely, yet with an unsatisfied longing in his eyes.

"Mr. Holbrook," he said, waiting after the rest had gone, "is there time for just one question?"

"Yes, for two, if you like," said Mr. Holbrook, sitting down again. "What is it, Edward?"

"I want to know why God don't answer folks' prayers right away?"

Mr. Holbrook smiled. "If your questions are all as hard as that, Edward, I don't think there will be time for another today. But there may be several reasons; we will try to find them. Sometimes God doesn't answer our prayers at once, simply to try our faith; to see whether we are willing to take him at his word and keep on asking until he is ready to give; or whether we will grow tired in a little while and give it up. And sometimes we spend all our strength in praying, and don't work; then, often, we don't believe we shall get what we are praying for. Do you understand me?"

"No, sir," answered Tip promptly.

"Well, let me see if I can make it plainer. For whom are you praying, Edward, that you are troubled this morning because you have not been heard?"

"For Kitty; I have been, this long time. Kitty's my sister, and I want her to love Jesus; but it don't seem to do any good for me to pray for her."

"It is *possible* that God may be trying your patience, but not probable; I think we can find a better reason. Do you work while you pray? I mean, do you talk with Kitty; tell her what you are praying for—urge her to come to Christ—try to show her how?"

Tip looked grave. "I did talk a little to her once, but it didn't seem to do her any good, and I haven't said a word since."

"Did you ever read in the Bible what is said about such praying, about saying, 'Depart in peace, be ye warmed and filled,' and not *doing* anything?"

Tip shook his head, and Mr. Holbrook held out his hand for the little Bible.

"Let me find it for you, and when you go home you may read it and see if you, in praying for Kitty and never saying a word to her, are not a little like that man. Then there's another thing. Do you really believe that God will do what you ask him? You say every day in your prayer, 'O God, make Kitty a Christian,' and yet, wouldn't you be very much astonished if Kitty should come to you today and say, 'I want to be a Christian?' Are you looking out for any such thing?"

Tip generally spoke his honest thoughts.

"No," he said gravely, "I ain't."

The church bell began to ring, and Mr. Holbrook arose. "I think if you begin to work and pray together, and then ask God to help you believe, that he will surely do as he has promised, that you will soon find your prayers answered."

This he said while gathering up his books and papers ready to start, and then:

"Edward, why don't you come to our Thursday evening prayer meetings?"

Tip's eyes were full of astonishment.

"I never once thought of it," he said. "Why, Mr. Holbrook, boys don't go, do they?"

"No," said the minister sadly; "they don't, because I don't know of another boy of your age in this whole town who loves the Savior. Only think what a work there is for you to do!"

Tip went home with his brain full of new thoughts. No, he didn't go home; he only went as far as the elm tree, and there he sat down and read what Mr. Holbrook had marked in his Bible. Yes, that was just the way in which he had been praying for Kitty; and it was certainly true, as Mr. Holbrook had said, nothing could surprise him more than that Kitty should really and truly come to Jesus.

Before he went from under the tree that day, he prayed this prayer: "O God, teach me to believe that you will make Kitty love Jesus, and show me how to help her."

After this, of course, he looked out for his chances in which to work, and of course he found them; found one that very day. After dinner Kitty wandered off by herself. Tip watched her, and she took the road leading to the cemetery. God put it into his heart to hurry after her; so when he came up to her, where she sat on a large stone which she had rolled very near to Johnny's grave, his heart was beating at the thought of the great work which he had to do.

"What did *you* come for?" said Kitty, looking up.

Tip hesitated a minute, then told the plain truth.

"I came after you."

"I suppose I know that; you didn't come before me."

"I mean I came to *see* you."

"Well, look at me, then, and go off; I don't want you here."

Clearly, whatever was to be said must be said quickly, and Tip's heart was very full of its message, so his voice was tender.

"Oh, Kitty, I came to ask you if you *wouldn't* be a Christian. I *do* want it so, it seems as if I couldn't wait."

Kitty looked steadily and gravely at her brother. "What do you mean by 'be a Christian'?" she asked at last.

"I mean, love Jesus, and do as he says."

"What'll I love him for?"

"'Cause you can't help it when you find out how much he loves you and all the things he does for you."

"What does he say to do?"

"He says be good; try to do right things all the time."

Kitty's eyes flashed. "Now ain't you mean!" she said angrily, "to come and tell me such things when you know I ain't good and *can't* be good. Isn't Mother ugly and cross and scolding to me all the time? And don't I have to work and work, *always,* and never have anything? And I'm cross and get mad, and I *will,* too. I can't help it."

"Oh, but, Kitty!" Tip interrupted eagerly, "you don't know about it; he helps you, Jesus does. When anything is the matter, when you feel cross and bad, you just go and kneel down and tell him all about it, and he helps you every time. And up in heaven, where you can go when you die, nobody ever gets cross and scolds; and it's beautiful there—they sing, and have fountains, and wear gold crowns, and—and Johnny is there, you know, and I'm going, and I *do* want you to come along."

Kitty's face had been growing graver and graver with every word her brother spoke, and when at last he stopped, with his eyes turned toward Johnny's little grave, Kitty's shawl was crumpled up in her two hands and held tightly to her face; and she was crying, not softly and quietly, but rocking herself back and forth and giving way to great sobs which shook her little form.

Tip looked distressed; he didn't know what to say next. He stooped down to her at last and spoke softly, "Oh, Kitty! I'm sorry for you; if you only *would* love Jesus it would make you happy."

"I want to, I want to," sobbed Kitty; "I would if I knew how."

Tip's heart gave a bound of joy; a surprised bound, too—he had not expected it so soon.

"It's easy, Kitty; it is, truly, if you only just ask God to do it. You see, he can hear every word you say; he hears you now, but he wants you to ask him about it. Say, Kitty, I'll go off and leave you—I'll go where I can't see nor hear you—then you kneel down and tell Jesus about it, and he'll help you."

"Stop!" said Kitty as Tip was turning away; "wait, I don't know what to say."

"Why, just *tell* him, just as you did me, and ask him to help you. You see, Kitty, you can't do a thing without that; he's got to look after you every single minute, or it's nothing at all."

Tip went away, and Kitty was left alone, alone in the

spot where her brother had first found the Savior. She felt very strangely; she had been left there alone to offer her first prayer.

Kitty had never been taught to kneel down by her bedside every evening and repeat "Our Father"; it was all new and strange to her. She sat still a long time, with the sober look deepening on her face. At last she got down on her knees and rested her little hard hands on the hard snow which covered Johnny's bed, and she said, "Jesus, I want to be what Tip says. I want to love you if you'll let me. Nobody loves me, I guess. Tip says you'll help me all the time. If you will, I'll try."

After she had said this, slowly and thoughtfully, stopping long between each sentence, she didn't feel like rising up; she wanted to say more, so she repeated it, adding, "Tip says I must be good. I can't be good, but I'll try."

Over and over was the simple, earnest prayer repeated.

Tip did not go back to Johnny's grave; he took a side road down through the edge of the grove and so went home; and when he reached home, he went up to his attic room and knelt down and prayed for Kitty as only those *can* pray who have been working, as well as asking, for what they want.

Kitty was stirring the pudding for supper when he saw her again; stirring away hard at the heavy mass which grew thicker and harder to stir every moment. He went over to her.

"Kitty, let me do this," and she gave up the pudding stick. Tip stirred away.

By and by she leaned over the kettle to put in some salt, and as she sprinkled it around she caught his eager, longing look. She nodded her head. "I guess he heard," she said softly.

"I *know* he did," Tip answered, his eyes very bright; in his heart he sang, *"Glory."* And the angels in heaven sang for joy, for that night there had been laid aside a white robe and a crown of gold for Kitty Lewis.

16

TIP was very undecided what to do. He went out on the steps and looked about him in the moonlight; then he came in and took a long look out of the window. At last the question, whatever it was, seemed to be settled; he turned with a resolute air to Kitty, who was washing the tea dishes.

"Kitty, don't you want to go to prayer meeting up at the church?"

Kitty dropped her cup back into the dishpan and stood looking at him, a good deal surprised; at last she said:

"I'd like to, Tip, but I don't look decent to go anywhere. I've only this dress and my old hood."

"I wouldn't mind that," said Tip. "I've only this awful old jacket either, but I mean to go; hurry up the dishes, and let's go."

"Well," said Kitty at last, "I *will;* but what will Mother say?"

"I'll fix that." And Tip stepped softly into the bedroom. "Are you better tonight, Father?"

"Not much better, I guess. How's arithmetic to-day?"

"First-rate; Mr. Burrows said I was getting ahead fast. Mother, may Kitty go out with me tonight? I'm going up to the church to prayer meeting."

Mrs. Lewis turned from the basket where she had been hunting long, and as yet in vain, for a piece of flannel and bent a searching, bewildered look on her son.

"I don't care," she said at last; "she can go if she likes; but I doubt if she will."

She *did,* however; in ten minutes more the two were walking along the snowy path. Kitty was sober. "Tip," she said presently, "don't you never get real awful *mad,* so mad that you feel as if you'd choke if you couldn't speak right out at somebody?"

"Well, no," said Tip, "not often; yes, I do, too; I get mad at Bob Turner sometimes, mad enough to pitch him into a snowbank; but it don't last long."

"Well, mine does," said Kitty. "I begin in the morning; something makes me cross, and I keep on getting crosser and crosser every minute, till it seems as if I should fly. Do you suppose I'll always do just so?"

"No," answered Tip positively, "I *don't.* You keep on trying a little bit harder every day, and by and by you'll find that you don't get cross more than half as easy as you used to. I know it will be so, because I've tried it in other things; when I first began to behave myself in school it was the *hardest* work—my! You can't think how I wanted to whisper, and things kept happening all the time to make me laugh, but I just keep trying, and now I hardly ever think of whispering. Kitty, does Mother know?"

"No," said Kitty, "she don't."

"If I were you I'd tell her."

"Oh, Tip, I can't; she never looks at me without scolding me; I can't talk to her about this."

"Yes, you can; I'd surely do it if I were you; it will be a great deal easier to try hard if Mother knows you are trying."

They were almost at the church door.

"Kitty," said Tip suddenly, "let's pray for Father tonight. I've been praying for him this long time; you help me."

Step by step, God was leading Tip Lewis in the narrow way. No sooner was he seated in the bright, warm little room and had listened to Mr. Holbrook's earnest prayer that every Christian there might do something for Christ that night than the struggle began; what ought he to do for Christ? People all around him were, one after another, offering prayer or saying a few words. Ought he to? Could he? Oh, he couldn't! Who would want to listen to him? It wouldn't do any good. There was Mr. Burrows right in front of him; he would be ashamed of him, perhaps. Yes, but then, ought he not to own his Savior? Mr. Holbrook had spoken of the verse, "Whosoever will deny me before men," and had made the meaning very plain. Mr. Minturn had just prayed that no one there might be ashamed of Christ. The end of it all was that Tip slipped off his seat down on his knees and said, "Our Father which art in heaven, hallowed be thy name. Show me how to pray. I don't want to deny Christ. I want to love him. I want the boys in our school, and my father, and everybody to love him. I'll try to work for Jesus. I'll try to work for him. Help me every day, and forgive my sins for Jesus' sake. Amen."

Tip had never felt so near to God as he did when he arose from his knees. Mr. Holbrook's voice trembled with feeling when, soon after, he prayed for the young disciple who had early taken up his cross.

At the close of the meeting, the minister pressed his way through the little company of people who were waiting to speak with him.

"Good evening, all," he said hurriedly, "excuse me tonight, brother," to Mr. Minturn, who would have stopped him anyway; "I want to speak to some people before they get away from me"—and those who watched saw him hurry on until he overtook Tip Lewis and his sister.

"Good evening, Edward; this is Kitty, I think. How do you do, my little girl? Edward, do you know such a Bible verse as this: 'I love the Lord, because he has heard my voice and my supplication?'"

"No, sir," answered Tip eagerly; "*is* there such a verse?"

"Yes, somewhere in the Psalms you will find it. I don't remember just where. Can you feel the truth of it when you think of your sister?"

"Yes, sir, I *can*. God *did* hear me."

"And you think you love Jesus tonight, Kitty?"

Kitty felt a great awe for the minister, and her "yes, sir" was low and spoken in a timid voice.

"What makes you think so?"

"I—I don't know; only I pray, and he hears me, and I like to."

"Well, now, Kitty, almost the first thing which people think of after they have found Jesus is something to do for him; they begin to look around to see what they can find. What are you going to do?"

"I don't know, sir; I haven't got anything I can do."

"Ah! that's a mistake; you can find plenty of work if you look for it; only don't look too far, because it is the little bits of things which come right in your way that Jesus wants you to do. When you brush up the room, and set the table neatly, and brighten the fire, and do little thoughtful things that help your mother—then you are pleasing Jesus, doing work for him. Isn't it pleasant to think that in all those little things, he is watching over you and that you make him glad when you do them well? Do you know that one of God's commands is, 'Honour thy father and thy mother'?"

"No," said Kitty softly.

"It is; those are the very words; Edward can find them for you in the Bible—and honor means more than obey; it means, try to please them in the very smallest things."

They were very near the corner where Mr. Holbrook must leave them. He laid his hand gently on Tip's shoulder as he said, "Speaking of Bible verses, Edward, I have one for you this evening, in the Savior's own words: 'Whosoever shall confess me before men, him will I confess also before my Father which is in heaven.' Good night."

Tip understood him, and there was a bright look in his eyes. The two walked on in silence for a little. Presently Kitty said, "I guess Mr. Holbrook don't know just how Mother is, or he wouldn't talk so."

"Yes, but," said Tip quickly, "God knew all about it always, you know; and yet he said that verse."

"So he did," answered Kitty gravely.

17

Behold, how great a matter a little fire kindleth.

"BAH," said Will Bailey, "you're fooling, Howard Minturn!"

"As true as I live, I'm not," answered Howard earnestly; "you can ask Mr. Burrows."

"What's up?" inquired Ellis Holbrook, joining the two.

"Why, Howard is telling the biggest yarn you ever heard; he says Tip Lewis went to prayer meeting last night and made a prayer."

"Tip Lewis!" and Ellis Holbrook's voice was full, not only of surprise, but scorn; "I should like to hear him."

"Well, it's true," repeated Howard. "My father told us about it this morning, and he said it was a good prayer, too—he said, Ellis, that your father couldn't keep the tears out of his eyes when he heard him, and Mr. Burrows walked uptown with Father and told him that Tip had changed wonderfully, that he was one of the best boys in school."

"Well," said Will Bailey, "if Tip Lewis has turned saint, I'll give up. Why, he's the meanest scamp in town—my father says he's bad enough for anything."

"Oh, well now," answered Ellis, "there's no use in

being stupid enough not to see that what Mr. Burrows says is true. I never saw anyone change as he has in my life, but I'll be hanged if I like him as well as I did before he was so awful good; he's too nice for anything nowadays."

"Especially when he trips *you,* the minister's son, up, about twisting the Bible."

Ellis's face glowed, but he was an honest boy. "He was right enough about that," he said promptly; "my father says it's wrong; but if it will do you any good to know it, I haven't liked Tip so well since."

"Say, Tip!" said Will Bailey, hailing him at recess, "come here and give an account of yourself; they say you turned parson last night. Did you?"

"No," said Tip with the greatest good humor, "I didn't."

"Didn't you speak in meeting?"

A quiet gravity spread itself over Tip's face. "I prayed in meeting," he answered, soberly.

"Oh! well, what did you pray for? Come, let's know."

"I prayed for *you.*" Tip spoke with quiet dignity.

"Humph! Now that's clever, certainly; much obliged."

And Will said no more.

Certainly, the boys had never talked so much about any prayer meeting in their lives as they did about this one. So that was the way it commenced; such a little fire kindled it. Tip didn't know it; he never found it out; probably he never will, until he takes his crown in heaven. From the humble little prayer which Tip had offered sprang the first buddings of the great revival which God sent down to them.

"Say," said Howard Minturn to Ellis on the next Thursday evening, "let's go over to prayer meeting tonight; I really am dreadfully anxious to hear Tip speak."

"No," answered Ellis, speaking heartily, more heartily than he often did to Howard, "I'm sure I don't care in the least to hear him, and I have enough to do without going there."

Howard was *determined* to go and to find company.

"Will, let's go to meeting tonight," he said the next time he came across Will Bailey.

Will looked at him in amazement. "What for?"

"To hear Tip."

"Oh!" said Will, "good! I'll go; let's get a lot of boys and go over; just to encourage him, you know."

And they went. Tip and Kitty were there again; and again, with Tip, the struggle had to be gone through; his coward spirit whispered to him that the boys would only make fun of him if he said a word and it would do more harm than good. His conscience answered, "Whosoever will deny me on earth, him will I also deny before my Father which is in heaven." The solemn words conquered, and again Tip knelt down and prayed.

"My!" said Mr. Minturn, talking with his wife after they reached home, "when I thought of the bringing up which that boy has had—no bringing up about it, he has just *come* up, the easiest way he could—but when I heard him pray tonight, and then thought of our boy, who has been prayed for and watched over every day since he was born, I declare I felt as though I would give all I'm worth to have Howard stand where Tip Lewis does now."

Howard heard this as he waited in the sitting room for his father and mother; heard it in great amazement, and at first it made him indignant. The idea of comparing *him* with Tip Lewis! Then it made him sorrowful; his father's tones were *so* sad; after all that had been done for him, it *was* hard that he should disappoint his parents.

He listened to his father's prayer that night very closely, and its earnestness brought the tears to his eyes. Altogether, Howard went to school the next morning with a somewhat sober face and took no part whatever in the boys' fun over the meeting.

Mr. Burrows's heart had been warmed by the voice of prayer from one of his scholars, and he began to pray and long for others of them to work also; and the great God, who knows the beginning and the end, led his first words of anxiety to Howard Minturn. They stood at the desk, teacher and scholar, Howard bending over his slate.

"Can't you get it?" Mr. Burrows asked.

"No, sir."

"Howard, are you working with all your thoughts today?"

"No, sir." And a bright flush mounted to his forehead.

"What is it, Howard?"

"I don't know, sir; not much of anything, I guess."

"Are you not quite satisfied with yourself today?"

"Satisfied! I—why—I don't know what you mean, sir; I have tried to do the best I could, I believe."

"Do you really think so, Howard?"

"Yes, sir."

"Did you think so last evening, in the prayer meeting? Can a boy who is as well taught as you have been feel that he is doing as well as he can, when he knows that he is every day cheating God?"

Howard's face fairly burned.

"I don't understand you, sir."

"Don't you?" and Mr. Burrows's voice was very

kind. "I wish that God's own Spirit might help you to understand it. Didn't your father and mother promise God, when you were born, to try to train you up for him, because you belonged to him and they knew it? Now, haven't they done their duty? Is it their fault that you are not a Christian?"

"No, sir."

"Then it comes back to you. You belong to God, body and soul; he made you; he has kept you; he would save you, only you will not let him. You can't help the fact that you belong to him; all you can do is to refuse to give him your love and let him lead you to heaven, and this you are doing. Is it right?"

Howard was growing haughty.

"I don't feel the need of any such things, Mr. Burrows," he answered coldly.

"Suppose you don't, does that help the matter any? Does it change the fact that you belong to God; that you are cheating him out of his own property? The question I ask is, are you doing right?"

Howard stood with eyes fixed on his slate, saying nothing.

"Won't you answer me, Howard?" Mr. Burrows asked gently. "Is it right?"

And after a long, long silence, the boy's honest, earnest eyes were raised to his teacher's face, and he spoke steadily.

"No, sir."

"Are you willing to go on doing wrong?"

"No, sir."

"Will you turn *now*, Howard, and start right?"

Now came another long silence. Howard Minturn, the honest, faithful boy, always getting a little nearer right than any of the others, had been condemned by his own words and knew not what to say. At last he spoke. "I can't promise, Mr. Burrows."

"Howard! Such an answer from *you,* to whom I have only needed to point out what was right in order to have it done!"

"But I can't trust myself, sir; I shall not feel tomorrow as I do now."

"That is, you feel like doing your duty today, but you expect if you wait until tomorrow that you will feel less like it; so you mean to wait. Is that right?"

The silence was much longer this time; so long that the boys began to look curiously at the two figures over by the desk and wonder why the bell was not rung. But at last he raised those clear, truthful eyes once more.

"Mr. Burrows, I'll try."

And the next Thursday evening when, in the house of prayer, it was very still because Mr. Holbrook had just said, "Is there not *one* here tonight who wants us to pray for him, and if there is, will he not let us know it *now?*" suddenly there was a row of astonished faces in the seat where the schoolboys were sitting because from among them arose Howard Minturn, and his face was pale and grave, and his voice was steady; they all heard his words:

"I want to be a Christian; will you pray for me?"

Oh, wouldn't they! Was there ever such another prayer as that which Mr. Minturn offered for his son! Did anyone who heard it wonder that such prayer was answered? and that in the next meeting, Howard, speaking with a little ring of joy in his voice, said, "I love Jesus tonight. I want everyone to love him. I am very happy."

From this the work went on. The little lecture room grew full and overflowed, and the crowd now filled the church; and every night some new voice was heard, asking for prayer.

Will Bailey seemed filled with the spirit of torment; teased the boys unmercifully, went to the meeting every evening, and made fun of it all day; but the boys were praying for him, and God's pitying eye was on him.

One evening there were two who arose to ask the prayers of Christians; one was Will Bailey, the most hopeless, so the boys thought, of all the boys in town; the other was Will Bailey's gray-haired father, the most hopeless, so the good men feared, of all the strong, self-satisfied men in town.

Yet there were two, for whom daily, earnest prayer was offered, who, in this blessed time, held themselves aloof; two boys, so far separated that it seems strange and sad that their names should be coupled just here. Bob Turner and Ellis Holbrook, the lowest and the highest; the worst boy in school and the best! Yet they were united in this one thing, that they would have nothing to do with Christ. Tip had prayed for both, worked for both; but this was his success one afternoon:

"Say, Bob, won't you go to meeting tonight, just to please me?"

"Couldn't, Tip, no way in the world. I'd do most anything to please you, too, for the sake of old times when we used to steal apples together; but I've promised to go with Nick Hunt tonight and tie old Barlow's cat fast to his front doorknob, and that's got to be done while the old man is at the meeting, you know. 'Tain't no matter, either, about my going; you just do the praying for you and me, too; then it will be all right."

Tip turned away with a sigh and a shudder. Could

it be possible that *that* boy had ever been his only companion! Ellis was round by the ball ground, and he went thither.

"Ellis, won't you go down tonight with the boys? It's almost the last meeting, you know."

Ellis wheeled around and spoke in his coldest tone:

"Tip Lewis, you seem to take a wonderful interest in me, and I'm sure I'm much obliged to you; but I'll be a great deal more so if you'll attend to your own affairs after this and let mine alone."

Poor Tip! How discouraged he felt. Yet that very evening, going home from school, he met Mr. Holbrook; the minister turned and walked uptown with him.

"Edward," he said, "are you praying for my boy?"

"Yes, sir."

"Will you never stop praying for him while you live, until he comes to Christ?"

"I never *will,* sir," answered Tip with energy.

18

Thy father and thy mother shall be glad,
and she that bare thee shall rejoice.

HOW did Mr. Holbrook know so well what Kitty needed to help her? His words had given her such new thoughts; some way it was all new to her, the idea that she had any duty to perform toward her mother. She stood thinking of it that bright winter day, stood before the little fire and wondered how it was that she ought to commence. She was to be alone all day. Mrs. Stebbens, their next neighbor, had fallen down and sprained her ankle and sent to know if Mrs. Lewis could do her promised day's work in the village. Kitty was left in charge of the house and her sick father. She looked around the room; what an ugly, dreary little room it was—dust, dirt, and cobwebs everywhere; her hood and shawl lying in one corner; her mother's apron on the floor in the middle of the room; the breakfast dishes not yet washed; the stove all spattered with grease from the pork gravy; the hearth thickly covered with ashes; the paper window curtain hanging by one tack; and on the mantelpiece, behind the stove, such an array of half-eaten apples, matches, forks, sticky spoons, broken teacups, and dirty candlesticks, as would have frightened anyone less used to it than was Kitty. As she looked around her, a forlorn smile came over her face, for she thought of Mr. Holbrook's words: "When you brush up the floor, or brighten the fire to please your mother—"

"He don't know," she said to herself, "that Mother don't care for sweeping and such things; he don't know how we live. I wonder if Mother *would* notice now if things were different; what if we did live like other folks—had nice things, and kept them put up, and the room swept; suppose I try it. What could I do? I might sweep and wash off the stove, and—clean off the mantelpiece. I'll just do it! and see if anybody in this house will care."

No sooner thought than commenced. Kitty went to work. The dishes were washed until they shone; those clean dishes shouldn't go in such a disorderly cupboard. There was no help for it, the shelves must be washed; down came the bottles and bundles, papers of this and boxes of that, which had been gathering Kitty didn't know how long, and the astonished shelves felt soap and water once more. How they were scrubbed!

"Kitty?" called her father from his bedroom, hearing the racket, "what are you doing?"

"I'm cleaning house," answered Kitty promptly.

And her father, because he did not know what else to do, let her work. From the cupboard she went to the mantelpiece, bundled the things all off in a heap, washed it thoroughly, and put everything in order. What a day it was to Kitty! One improvement led to another, and as things began to grow clean in her hands, she grew wonderfully interested and only stopped at noon to warm her father's gruel.

It was Saturday, and Tip had gone to pile wood for Mr. Bailey. He was to get his dinner and a grammar for his pay. He had wanted a grammar all winter, so he worked with a will; and Kitty saw neither him nor her mother through all the busy day. The early sun had set long before. Kitty thought he certainly would not know that room the next morning, it was all so changed. The paper curtain was mended and tacked up in its place; the old lounge cover was mended and fastened on smoothly; the mantelpiece shone and glowed in the firelight; the two shiny candlesticks, and beside them the little box of matches, were all that remained there of the rubbish of the morning; the floor was just as smooth and clean as soap and ashes, with plenty of hot water and an old broom could make it; hoods, and shawls, and aprons, and old shoes had all disappeared; nothing was lying around—the table was drawn out, the clean, smooth plates arranged so as to hide the soiled spots on the tablecloth, the pudding was bubbling away in the astonished kettle, and Kitty's joy had been complete when, only a few minutes before, after a great deal of stamping and pounding, she had opened the door to Howard Minturn, who said:

"Mother sent you some milk for your supper— Where's Tip?—*Isn't* it cold though?—There'll be prime skating tonight—Give me the pitcher right away, please." All this in one breath.

Now they would have beautiful fresh milk for supper, and if there was anything which Tip liked, it was pudding and milk.

So Kitty set the old armchair in the warmest corner for her mother, fastened her father's door wide open so he could see the new room, then stirred her pudding, and watched and waited. Her mother came first. Kitty's heart had never beat more anxiously than when she heard the slow, tired step on the hard snow. Would she notice anything different? In she came, tired, cross, and cold, expecting to find disorder, discomfort, and cold inside. Could anybody, having eyes, fail to notice the changes which had been wrought in that little room since she went out from it in the early morning? She shut the door with a little slam, and then the flush of the firelight seemed to blind her a little; she brushed her hand over her face and looked around her with a bewildered air. Kitty went over to her; some way she felt a great kindness in her heart for her mother, a great longing to do something for her.

"Is it cold, Mother?" she asked brightly. "Take that chair," pointing to the seat in the warm corner. "Supper's all ready, and I've made a cup of tea for you."

Mrs. Lewis took off her hood and shawl in silence, untied her wet shoes, and placed her cold feet on the clean, warm stove-hearth; took in the brightness of the room, the shiny candlesticks, the neatly spread tea table—took whiffs of the steaming tea, all in utter silence. Only, when Kitty's father, looking out, said, "There's been business done here since you went away," something in her mother's voice as she answered, "I should think there had," made the blood rush warmly into Kitty's cheeks and made her whisper to herself as she stooped to place the wet shoes under the stove to dry, "Mr. Holbrook told me true, I do believe. I guess I have pleased Jesus today; I feel so."

While she was taking up the pudding, there was a merry whistle outside, a brisk, crushing step on the snow, and Tip whizzed into the room.

Oh, there was no mistaking the look of delight on his face, nor the glad ring in his voice as he said, "Oh, Kitty! Why, Kitty Lewis! What *have* you been doing? Why, it looks most as nice here as it does at Howard Minturn's."

All that evening there seemed a spell upon the

Lewis family. Mrs. Lewis didn't say one cross or fretful word; indeed, she had no cause, for in Kitty's heart there was a strange, new feeling of love for her mother, of longing to please and give her comfort; and never was mother waited on with a more quiet care than Mrs. Lewis received that night.

This was the first coming of home comfort to the family. Tip had apples in his pocket, which Howard Minturn had given him; he roasted them before the fire, and his father ate very little pieces of them; and his mother darned stockings by the light of the candle in the clean little candlestick set on the clean little stand; and they were happy.

By and by Tip brought out his grammar and, finding Kitty very much interested in examining it, said:

"What if you should begin and study grammar with me?"

"What if I should?" answered Kitty. So that evening she commenced her education, and, though grammar was a queer study to *begin* with, still it was a beginning.

The pleasant evening wore away; the town clock had struck nine, Kitty's father had gone quietly to sleep, and the bedroom door was shut to keep all sounds from disturbing him. Tip had taken his candle and gone. Mrs. Lewis sat toasting her feet before the dying fire, yet still Kitty lingered. She wanted to take Tip's advice and tell her mother about her dear, new friend, and this evening of such wonderful peace seemed the good time for doing so; but she didn't know how—if her mother would only say something to her! and presently she did.

"Kitty, what fit came over you, to go to work and clear up at such a rate?"

"I wanted to please *you,* I guess."

Kitty knew that this answer would surprise her

mother, and it did, into utter silence; but after what seemed to Kitty a long, *long* time, she spoke again.

"What did you want to do that for?"

Now for it! This was the best chance she could ever hope to have, and her voice trembled a little.

"I wanted to please Jesus, too, Mother, and Mr. Holbrook said if I did things to help you, and that you would like, *he* would be glad—Jesus would, you know." A little silence, and then, "I want to please Jesus all the time now because I love him, and I'm going to try to do right."

It was all out now, and her heart was beating so that it almost stopped her voice. Her mother shaded her face with her hand and neither spoke nor moved. Kitty waited a little, then moved slowly toward the door of her bit of bedroom; it was moonlight, so she needed no candle.

"Good night, Mother," she found courage to say at last.

"Good night," and her mother's voice sounded strange, coming from behind the closely held hand.

There was something like a great sob in Kitty's throat as she went to her room that night—in her heart was a great longing for mother love. She would have liked to kiss her mother good night, but she felt how queer that would look; even to *say* good night was something very unusual. So she knelt down beside her bed and prayed for her mother.

I don't think Mr. Holbrook knew that the few kind words which he spoke to Kitty Lewis on her way home from prayer meeting were seeds which were going to spring up and bear fruit into everlasting life.

19

And all thy children shall be taught of the Lord.

"FATHER," said Tip as, after having carefully measured out and given him some cough drops, he sat down for a chat with him before school, "Father, didn't you and Mr. Bailey go to school together when you were boys?"

"Yes," said Mr. Lewis. "Our fathers lived side by side, and we used to walk more than a mile to school together every morning—we were in the same class, too, and the best scholars in school. My! times are changed since that day—my father was considerably better off than his was, and now he's a rich man and I'm nobody."

"Was he such a boy as Will Bailey is—or, I mean, as Will used to be?"

"I don't know much about Will; but I know his father was a sorry scamp, and many's the scrape he got me into. He took a notion to me; we lived nearby and were always together; and then I was full of pranks as he was, I suppose; but he was a regular tyrant over the rest of the boys; they were more than half afraid of him; I don't know but what I was myself. Anyhow, I know I've thought I'd have been different, maybe, if I hadn't followed him so close in all his scrapes."

"Father, did you know Mr. Bailey was different now?"

"Different—how? What do you mean?"

"Why, he comes to prayer meeting, and speaks and prays, and seems to love to."

"The mischief he does!" said Mr. Lewis, surprised out of his usual quiet tone. "I should think he *was* different. Why, he used to make great fun of all such things."

"Yes, that's what he says; but I tell you, he don't make fun now."

"When did all that happen?"

"A few weeks ago, when the revival was, you know; he got up one night and asked them to pray for him, and now he most always speaks or prays in the meetings."

"Well," said Mr. Lewis after a pause and with a little sigh, "I'm sure I ain't sorry; I only hope it will last; he needed it as bad as anyone I know of."

"It will last," Tip said, speaking positively. "God will look out for that."

Then he waited a little while before he spoke again—but he had been praying for his father long enough and earnestly enough to feel bold.

"I thought, last night, that you must have been pretty good friends once," he said presently, "for he 'most broke down when he was praying for you, and the tears just blinded him."

Mr. Lewis turned himself on his pillow and looked steadily at his son. "Did Mr. Bailey pray for *me!*" he asked at last.

"Yes, he did, and he prayed as if he meant it."

"How came he to?"

"Why, I asked 'em to—all the folks in meeting, you know. I wanted you to be a Christian and prayed for you, and then I asked them if they'd pray, and Mr. Bailey got right up. You don't mind that, do you, Father? All the folks down there ask us to pray for their friends."

"No," answered Mr. Lewis at last, speaking slowly, "I don't know as I do. I need praying for, I suppose, if anybody does. I'm going where I can't be prayed for, pretty fast, I guess."

Tip had no answer to make to that.

"So you prayed for me too, did you?" his father asked presently.

"Yes, and I *do* every day, Father; I *do* want you to know Jesus."

A long silence followed, and then the sick man spoke again.

"Well, Tip, I'm glad that you've got right, gladder than I can tell you. My father was a good man and tried to make me do what was right; but I went all wrong, wasted my whole life, and brought up my children to do so too. But you're getting on without my help, and I'm glad you'll grow up to be a good man and be a comfort to your mother when I'm gone. But I don't know as you need ask folks to pray for me; it's too late. I've gone too far to get back."

Tip's bold, prompt manner did not forsake him now; he answered, quickly:

"Father, I don't believe any such thing. God doesn't say anything about its being too late, and he says if we want anything very much, and pray for it, and it's good to have, he'll give it to us; and I'm bound to believe him. Once I prayed for Kitty, and prayed and prayed, and it didn't do a bit of good, until at last Mr. Holbrook told me that maybe it was because I didn't really believe any of the time that God was going to do what I wanted him to; and I found out that was it.

Just as soon as I began to think he would hear me, it all came out straight; and now I'm bound to believe him every time. I've asked him to make you a Christian, and I'm going to keep on asking, and *he'll do it*. Father," Tip's voice took a softer tone, for he knew there was one very tender spot in his father's heart, "don't you want to see little Johnny up in heaven?"

The muscles around Mr. Lewis's mouth began to twitch nervously, and a tear rolled down his cheek.

"I'm pretty near it," he said at last, "and I think sometimes I'd give the world, if I had it, to be ready to go; but it's all too late. I've known the right way all my life, and I've gone the other way; now I must just take my pay."

The very Spirit of Christ must have shown Tip what to say next; he spoke the words earnestly and solemnly; he meant no disrespect:

"Father, do you know more about it than God? Because, you see, it don't say any such thing anywhere in the Bible; I know it don't, for we talked about it in Sunday school once, and Mr. Holbrook said, 'No matter how old a man was, nor what he had done, he could be a Christian.'"

"I always thought it looked mean and sneaking in a man, to have nothing to do with such things all his life, and then turn around just because he was going to die and pretend to be very good. God can't be pleased with any such thing as *that*. I've always said that I'd never do it."

Tip couldn't answer this; it didn't sound true; he felt sure it was not true; but he had no wisdom with which to meet it. He went to school with those last words of his father's ringing in his heart, and his thoughts took shape, and spoke in the very first sentence that he addressed to Mr. Holbrook, whom he overtook as he came out of the post office.

"Mr. Holbrook, can I ask you a question?"

And the minister, always ready to help anyone out of trouble, smiled and bowed, and walked on by the side of the troubled boy.

"If a man should tell you he thought it would be mean in him to turn around and go to serving God after he had found out he had but a little while to live, when he had cheated him out of all the rest of his life, what would you say?"

"I think," said Mr. Holbrook, "I would be very likely to ask him whether he supposed he would feel any less mean for cheating God out of the last year of his life, simply because he had been doing so all the other years; because a man has been doing wrong for forty years, I don't know why he should add another year of wrong; I should think he might much better turn around and make all the amends he could."

"Oh!" said Tip, drawing a long breath; "why couldn't I have thought of that? I knew it was wrong, I saw it plain enough; but I couldn't think of a word to say."

Mr. Holbrook looked earnestly at the eager boy. "Edward," he said at last, "do you think your father would see me this morning?"

"Yes," said Tip decidedly, "I know he would. If you would only go and see him, Mr. Holbrook, and explain that to him, I would be *so* glad."

And looking back soon after, he had the satisfaction of seeing Mr. Holbrook walk quickly downtown in the direction of his home. And now Tip felt hopeful for his father; he had prayed for him, he had worked for him, and now Mr. Holbrook had gone to him; surely, he could leave the rest in God's hands.

20

Let him that thinketh he standeth
take heed lest he fall.

"HERE, Tip!" said Howard Minturn, "hold this frame steady while I try that nail. Will, don't put that one up so high; it ain't even with the others. Hold on, Ellis— catch hold of this stool; it's tipping. There, now it's all nice and in order; isn't it, Mr. Burrows?" And he sprang from his stool as their teacher entered the schoolroom door.

"Very likely," answered Mr. Burrows smiling; "only I didn't hear what you said."

"I say we're ready for examination, room and all."

"The room is, certainly; and I hope your brains are. Ellis, I'd move that chair a little to the left; it will be in the way of the classes as it stands now. Do you feel brave today, Edward?"

"Yes, sir," answered Tip promptly; "pretty brave."

And he did, besides feeling eager and excited. The long winter term was over; today and tomorrow were to be days of examination; the boys had been working hard for it, none harder than had Tip. It was the first examination which had ever come to him in this exciting way. Always before he had been among the few inevitable dunces, running away from examination altogether, or else laughing good-naturedly over his own blundering ignorance. But today it was different; he stood there on the stage among the workers, proudly answering his teacher's questions and looking proudly over at the group of idlers—Bob Turner at their head—who loitered near the windows, wondering that he could ever have been of their number. This was going to be a great day for Tip; it is true he was far behind some others of his age, so far that not a single class of Howard Minturn's and Ellis Holbrook's were to be examined that day—the advance classes being put for the next day—while all of his came that morning; but then, Tip knew there was change enough in him to call the attention of everyone present; he felt the change in himself; his mother felt it when she that morning brushed his hair for him and fastened a clean collar on his jacket; the boys in school felt it. He had taken his place among the workers.

The bell rang at last, and the scholars filed in and took their places. There were visitors, even in the early morning; the people liked to attend Mr. Burrows's examinations. Tip's class in reading came first on the list, and never had his eyes been so bright or his face so eager. Tip had learned to read. Patiently, earnestly, he had plodded on through the long winter; now his sad blunderings in that line were over forever; not a boy in school read more slowly, distinctly, and correctly than Tip Lewis. The selections were to be made by the committee, immediately after class, of those who were considered ready to enter the history class on the following term. This was the highest reading class in the school, and Tip's eyes fairly danced when Mr. Holbrook, who was chairman of the committee, out of a class of thirteen read but two names: "Thomas Jones" and "Edward Lewis."

"Hallo, Tip!" Howard Minturn had said to him at recess. "Let's shake hands; welcome to history; it's awfully hard and interesting."

And Tip did shake hands, and laughed, and looked over at the other clique—the dunces—with a half-patronizing nod to Bob Turner, and wondered how he *could* have borne it to have been numbered with them that day; then he felt that he was climbing into the first set, and climbing *fast*.

In spelling, too, he came off conqueror; spelled down the class, spelled until Mr. Burrows closed his book with the words, "I presume you are tired of this, gentlemen, and as our examinations are confined to the lessons, I think it will hardly pay to go farther, for Edward has not missed since the second week in the term."

So again, flushed and excited, Tip went to his seat victorious. Only arithmetic now, and he would be through with the working part of the day. It was the last recitation in the morning, and he was so eager and anxious to do well that he began to grow nervous.

The class was called at last. They had gone slowly and carefully through long division and would be ready for fractions next term. The recitation passed off finely. Tip had not studied day and night during the winter for nothing. He was at the board, working an example in long division; it was almost finished. The hand of the clock pointed to ten minutes of twelve. In ten minutes he would be through, and his name would stand on that honored list, among those who had not missed one word or made one mistake during the examination! His hand began to tremble. What was the matter with that example? Oh, what *was* the matter! The remainder was too large; no, it was too small; no—it was—he didn't know what! Everybody was watching him; he heard a boy laugh softly. He had made a mistake, then; what was it? Where was it? Mr. Burrows's voice came to him, calm and kind.

"Edward, don't get excited; look at your remainder closely; take the first figures of divisor and remainder; nine in thirty-one, how many times? That will help you."

Ellis Holbrook stood but a step from the blackboard, just behind him. Tip heard his low whisper, "Seven," and without waiting to think—indeed he was too nervous to think—he caught at the number.

"Seven times!" he said hurriedly.

Then he heard bursts of laughter from the boys, and dashed down his chalk in an agony of shame and pain. And the clock struck twelve!

The honor was lost.

The boys gathered around him after school was closed.

"It was too bad, Tip," Howard Minturn said in a tone of honest sympathy. "You'd have had it in a minute more."

"I'd have had it if it had not been for Ellis Holbrook, and he's a mean scamp!" Tip answered in a rage.

"Whew!" said Will Bailey; "what did Ellis do?" and Ellis turned and proudly confronted the angry boy.

"He told me wrong just on purpose; that's what he did, and he knows it."

And Tip broke away from them and dashed out of the room.

Howard Minturn stood aghast! That Ellis Holbrook, his best friend and the very pink of honor among the boys, should do so mean a thing, he could not think, and yet it was hard to think that Tip had not told the truth.

"What does he mean, Ellis?" he asked at last.

"'You'll have to ask him if you find out,'" said Ellis haughtily. "He knows better than anybody else does what he means, I guess."

The boys started homeward presently in a body. Bob Turner and his friends surrounded Tip, and Bob, who never lost a good opportunity for teasing, commenced at once.

"Poor little fellow missed his lesson, so he did. Don't him cry; him shall have a penny to buy a multiplication table with."

"Hold your tongue!" answered Tip, too angry to see how foolish it was to let such words, coming from a boy who didn't know a single line of the multiplication table, provoke him.

"*Such* a pity!" began Bob again; "when it had spelled its lesson all so nice and had its face washed and its hair combed so pretty; mustn't cry, now, to spoil its face. Poor little fellow!"

Tip turned toward his tormenter a face perfectly white with rage, and the boys hardly knew his voice.

"Bob Turner, if you say another word I'll knock you down and thrash you within an inch of your life. I will—"

Oh, Tip Lewis! God forgive you for the way in which you, in your blind rage, have finished that sentence! For the use which you have made of that great name, which, above all others, you profess to reverence and fear. The awful word, once spoken, recalled him to himself; he clapped both hands over his face and ran wildly up the hill, then down out of sight.

The boys had all heard it. Howard, Ellis, Will Bailey, and a half dozen others were just behind him.

Ellis Holbrook's pride rose high.

"There's your wonderful boy," he said, "who was so changed and has taken it upon himself to preach so many sermons to *me*. I'm sure I never finished any of my angry speeches with an oath, if I *am* so far below him."

What an afternoon that was to Tip! He will *never* forget it. He went no farther than the great tree, which was budding out in spring green. Down he sat on a stone and once more covered his face with his hands, and such a storm of rage and pain swept over him as he had never known before.

"How could he, how *could* he have said that word?"

Ever since he had learned to pray, he had been afraid of that sin, afraid he might forget and go back to his old habits, and he had watched and guarded his lips with such care and prayer. But lately he had given up all fear; it had been such a long time, and he had never once fallen; he felt sure that he never would again.

He had felt so sure and proud and strong that he had asked no help from God that day; he had been so eager to spend every moment on his arithmetic that he had found no time to go to his Bible for strength. No wonder. Oh, no wonder that he fell! He had been standing too firmly, feeling no need of help. Now what should he do? How low he felt, how mean! Could God forgive him? Yes, he *could*.

Tip felt in his soul that there was nothing which God could *not* do, and yet he felt too mean and fallen to dare to ask him for anything more; he forgot, for the moment, that Jesus Christ died to save *sinners*.

The sun went on over his head and commenced his afternoon work; then there came up the hill the sound of the school bell, but Tip took no notice of that—he didn't want to *think* of school, even much less *go*. He began to fumble presently for his Bible; he *must* have some help. It opened of itself to the Psalms, and he read the first line which he saw, "Unto thee, O God, do we give thanks—" No, not that, and he turned back a couple of leaves. "Make a joyful noise—" No, no! he didn't want to hear anything about joy; his heart was as heavy as lead. So he turned over several leaves at once; he *must* find something that would read as if it meant him. "O Lord, rebuke me not in thy wrath; neither chasten me in thy hot displeasure." Oh, that was it! God was very angry with him—had a right to be—this was just what he ought to say. He read on through the psalm; almost every verse seemed for him, and when he read the one next to the last—"Forsake me not, O Lord: O my God, be not far from me"—he said it over and over, and finally, in a great burst of tears, got down and said it on his knees.

The short spring day was over, and the chilly night was setting in. Tip had reached home finally, had split the wood for the next day, done whatever he could find to do about the house, and then carried the vests which his mother had just finished to the clothing store—going away around behind the mill so as to avoid passing the schoolhouse, lest he might chance to see some of the boys. Then he came home, ate his supper in silence, and went up to his attic. He felt better than he had at noon, but his heart was still heavy, and he dreaded the next day, not knowing what he ought to do, nor how to do it. This was Thursday evening, but he didn't mean to go to prayer meeting. Kitty had asked him, had even coaxd a little, but he said, "No, not tonight." He felt stiff and sore from his long sitting under the great tree in the early spring dampness. He told himself that this was the reason why he was not going to prayer meeting; but the real one was, he felt as if he could not possibly face Mr. Burrows that evening, and *certainly* not Mr. Holbrook—of course, Ellis had told him all about it. He felt very tired, and his head and limbs ached; he was going to read a chapter in the Bible and go to bed. He chose the same psalm which had come to him with so much power that afternoon, read it slowly and carefully, then knelt down to pray, and as he did so, a new trouble loomed up before him. What should he do? He had prayed for Ellis Holbrook and Bob Turner ever since he began to pray for himself, but he felt as though he could not possibly pray for either of them tonight. Both had tried to injure him; both had succeeded; he wished them no harm, he didn't want to choke nor drown them, as he had felt like doing at noon, but clearly, he didn't want to pray for them. He had arisen from his knees and was sitting on the edge of the box which was his table and chair with a very troubled face. The more he thought about it, the more he felt that he could not pray for those boys just then. At last he thought he had found a way out of the difficulty. He said to himself that he was very tired, almost sick; he would just repeat the Lord's Prayer and go to bed; in the morning, very likely, he should feel differently. He almost knew he should. So he knelt down once more.

"Our Father, which art in heaven," slowly, reverently, through the sweet petition, until he came to "forgive us our debts as we—" There he stopped; he understood that prayer; they had been taking it up in Sunday school, a sentence at a time, and talking about it, and only Sunday before last that sentence had been explained. Tonight Tip could not finish it; there was no getting around the fact that he had not forgiven either Ellis or Bob. Once more he got up and took a seat on the edge of his bed to think. He was never so perplexed in his life. What ought he to do? Couldn't he pray at all? Mr. Holbrook had said he must never mock God by asking for what he did not mean, and to say those words, "as we forgive our debtors," feeling as he did tonight would be mocking God. He ought not to feel so, but how could he help it? Suddenly, with a little sigh of relief, he went down on his knees again; he had thought of something which he could say. "Oh, Jesus, make me feel like praying for Bob and Ellis; make me want them to be Christians as hard as I did last night; make me feel like forgiving them." Then there was silence in the lonely attic, while Tip, still on his knees, struggled with the evil spirit within him and came off conqueror, for presently he added, "Oh, dear Jesus, I'll forgive them both!" and then he finished the prayer. "Forgive us our debts, as we forgive our debtors." While he went around after that, making ready for rest and sleep, the "peace of God which passeth understanding" came down and settled in his heart. Presently he seemed to come to another difficulty, for he sat down with one boot in his hand and one still on his foot; this question, however, was settled promptly; he pulled up his jacket and put that on, seized his hat, and ran downstairs.

"Kitty," he said, putting his head in at the kitchen door, "I'm going, after all; come on."

And Kitty joyfully ran for her hood and shawl.

But Tip did not open his lips in prayer meeting that evening; he felt bowed down to the very ground with shame; he did not once raise his eyes to the seat where Howard Minturn, Will Bailey, and others of the schoolboys were sitting; and when the short hour was gone he made haste to get out from Mr. Holbrook's sight and the sound of his voice. But he had much reason, after that, to thank God that he did not succeed. He had just got from under the gaze of the hall lamp and stood a minute in the darkness waiting for Kitty when he felt Mr. Holbrook's hand on his arm and heard his kind, quiet voice.

"Edward, Mrs. Holbrook has some little business to transact with Kitty tonight; shall I walk with you?" And as Tip saw there was no help for it and walked by his side, he said, "I didn't see you at school this afternoon; how was that?"

"Mr. Holbrook, didn't Ellis tell you about it this noon?"

"Ellis has told me nothing. I heard, from one of the smaller boys, a very sad story. Have you anything to tell me?"

"No, sir, I have not; it's all true. I got awful mad, and I said mad things. I-I did worse than that."

Tip's voice sank to a solemn whisper. Mr. Holbrook, too, was silent and sad; at last he said:

"What, Edward! do you mean to give up and go back to the old life?"

And he remembered, years after, just how painfully his heart throbbed while he waited for Tip's answer; it was prompt and plain.

"No, sir; God wouldn't ever let me do that."

And then for a minute Mr. Holbrook did not speak for very thankfulness that, through all this maze of sin, God was leading Tip into the light again.

"Do you feel that you have God's forgiveness?" he asked, speaking gently.

"Yes, sir"; Tip could not give very long answers that evening.

"Why were you so quiet tonight in prayer meeting?"

"Because," said Tip, speaking low, "I was ashamed

to say anything before you or Mr. Burrows or the boys after what happened today."

"More ashamed with us than you were with God?"

"Yes, sir, I was; because God knows all about it—just how sorry I am, and how he has forgiven me and is going to help me, and you didn't know that."

Again Mr. Holbrook was thankful.

"How about tomorrow, Edward?" he asked at last.

And this time Tip's answer was very low. "I don't know; I don't know what to do."

"If you knew what was right to do, would you *do* it?"

"I'm pretty sure I'd *try* to, sir."

"Well, did you honor or dishonor Christ today?"

Tip's answer was in a more timid tone than he often spoke.

"I dishonored him."

"Do the boys know that you are very sorry and have asked God to forgive you?"

"No, sir; they don't know anything about it."

"Don't you think, for the honor of Christ, they ought to?"

"I suppose so."

"Who ought to tell them?"

No immediate answer came to this; then, after a little:

"Mr. Holbrook, how could I tell them—should I talk to each one about it?"

"See if you cannot answer your own question. Will not all the boys be likely to hear about it?"

"Yes, sir; they'll be sure to."

"And would they all be likely to hear what you have to say, unless you spoke to all at once?"

"But, Mr. Holbrook, if I did that, it would have to be in school."

"Well?"

"But tomorrow is the last day, and it's examination."

"Well?"

That short word seemed to have a good deal of power over Tip, for he only answered it by saying, after a long silence:

"Mr. Holbrook, I wonder if you can think how very hard that would be?"

"Edward, I wonder if you can think how very hard it was for your Savior to listen to your words this noon?"

And Mr. Holbrook heard no more from Tip, save, when they reached the corner, a very low, very grave, "Good night."

21

He shall call upon me, and I will answer him:
I will be with him in trouble;
I will deliver him, and honour him.

THERE were not many visitors in the next morning; it was too early as yet for any but the examining
committee and a few very fond, very anxious
mothers. Mr. Burrows's hand was on the bell; in a
few moments the algebra class would be in full tide
of recitation. Ellis and Howard had their slates in
their hands, ready to start at the first sound, when Tip
Lewis left his seat and made his way toward the stage.
Mr. Burrows looked surprised; this was entirely out
of order; but a look at Tip's face made him change
his mind about sending him back to his seat, and he
bent his head to listen to the few words that were
hurriedly whispered in his ear. Then he looked more
surprised, hesitated a minute, then asked:

"Hadn't you better wait until noon, and I can
detain the scholars a few moments?"

"No," said Tip, shaking his head and speaking earnestly; "I'm afraid if I wait till noon, I shan't do it at all."

"Very well," Mr. Burrows answered finally.
"Scholars, one of your number tells me that he has
something of importance to say to you; we will wait
and hear him."

It was well for Tip that he was a bold boy, that every day of his life had been such as to teach him a lesson of boldness, else his courage would surely have failed him when he felt the many curious eyes resting on him. As it was, his face was scarlet when he turned it away from the desk and toward the boys. Yet he spoke promptly, as he always did when he spoke at all.

"I want to tell the boys that I am sorry for yesterday. I suppose they all know what I did. I got awful mad, and I–I said a dreadful word. I didn't think I would ever be so wicked again; I feel awful about it. But I don't want the boys to think that I don't love Jesus anymore, because I do; and he is going to help me try again."

Such a silence as was in that schoolroom then the boys had never felt before! Mr. Burrows's face was shaded with his hand; he let the silence rest upon them for a moment after Tip had taken his seat; then he spoke, low and solemnly.

"Boys, what God has forgiven, I feel sure that no scholar of mine will be mean enough to ever mention again."

Then the bell sounded, and the business of the day went on. Tip had laid his head down on the desk the minute he took his seat, and he kept it there throughout the recitation. He had been through a fearful struggle; it was hard work for a boy like him to stand up before the school and tell them how he had fallen. But it was over now, and from his very soul he felt that he had done right.

Bob Turner, sitting beside him, was quiet and sober; and when Tip raised his arm with such a sudden jerk that he knocked his arithmetic to the floor, Bob leaned over and quietly picked it up and laid it back in its place, which was a wonderful thing for Bob Turner to do.

At noon the boys gathered around Tip, quiet and kind. No one spoke of what had been *the* important event of the morning; all were on good behavior.

Ellis Holbrook came into their midst.

"Tip," he said, speaking gravely yet very coldly, "perhaps it would be as well for you to know that you made quite a blunder yesterday when you said I told you wrong; I hadn't the slightest notion of telling you, right or wrong. But I know how you came to think so. I was looking up a word in Mr. Burrows's dictionary and stood just beyond you, when Mr. Bailey leaned over and asked me how many there were in your class when all were present, and I answered him, 'Seven.'"

Tip looked perfectly astonished.

"Why didn't you say so yesterday?" he asked at last.

"Because you didn't give me a chance," Ellis answered coolly. "I'm not in the habit of cheating, nor of being told that I do, so I was not prepared with an answer."

"That's true," said Tip after a minute, answering the first part of Ellis's sentence; "that's true, I didn't. I was mad, and I just banged off before anybody could say anything. I might have known you didn't do any such thing; it ain't like you."

And Tip walked away, leaving Ellis to think that the boy who was so far below him had shown much the better spirit of the two.

The busy day was drawing to a close; the last recitation was over, and the boys were in a state of grand excitement, waiting to hear the report of the committee; waiting to know whose names were to stand on the Roll of Honor, having passed through

the entire examination without a mistake. Poor Tip
was sad; yesterday morning he had felt so sure that
his name would have an honorable place, and to
him it was so much more exciting, because it would
be for the first time. How hard he had worked; and
now it was all lost! Stupidly lost, too, he said to
himself, over an example that he had done a dozen
times; and he drew a heavy sigh and roused himself
to listen to the report. Mr. Burrows had already
called for it, and Mr. Holbrook, as chairman of the
committee, had arisen, but, instead of reading the
report, said:

"Mr. Burrows, if there is time, I should like to say
a few words to the scholars. Boys, you were all
listeners to Edward Lewis's examination yesterday,
and I presume you know better than I do how hard
he has worked. Now, I think anyone who watched
him yesterday could not have failed to see that, had
he not grown excited and nervous, he could have
worked that example. Mr. Burrows, may I put a
question to vote?" And Mr. Burrows giving a hearty
consent, he continued, "Very well; now I want
every boy here who is willing to allow Edward
Lewis to go to the board *now* and try that example
and, if he succeeds, give him the place which would
have been his yesterday, to stand up."

Ellis Holbrook was the first to spring to his feet,
and every single boy in the room followed his
example; Tip alone sitting still, with burning cheeks.

"Well done," said Mr. Holbrook. "Now it only
remains to get your teacher's consent to our plan."

Which Mr. Burrows gave by wheeling his table
from before the blackboard and picking up an arithmetic. "You may come forward, Edward; I will dictate
the example; which one is it?"

"The thirty-ninth, sir; fifty-first page."

By this time Tip was at the board. How they watched him; how fearful his teacher was for him; how he longed to have him succeed! Tip worked fast and boldly; his hand did not tremble; chalk and fingers and brain did their duty; the terrible "nine in thirty-one, how many times" as a test for the larger number was reached, and an unusually large and bold figure *three* was placed in the quotient; a few more rapid dashes, and with a grand flourish after the "seventeen remainder," Tip threw down the chalk, pushed back the hair from his hot temples, and walked to his seat. The boys could not keep quiet any longer. A very soft tapping was heard at first; then, finding they were not silenced, it rose to a loud decided stamping of many feet. But Mr. Holbrook was on *his* feet again, and they were quiet directly, for the report was finally to be read.

"My son," said Mr. Holbrook not long after, laying his hand kindly on Ellis's shoulder, as he was hurrying from the room, "what do you think of Edward's religion tonight?"

"I think it is honest, sir," Ellis answered quickly. "Excuse me, Father, if you please; I must see Howard a minute before he goes," and so he ran away from his father's longing look.

As for Tip, he borrowed from Howard Minturn a copy of the village paper, which came out a few days after, and read the report of the examination; read this sentence: "And, among all the pupils, perhaps no one of them has made more rapid or astonishing progress than has Edward Lewis."

Then, while the twilight deepened, he turned eagerly to the next column, which read in this way:

"Roll of Honor:

Being an alphabetically arranged list of those who passed the entire examination without making an error.

Willard Bailey,
Ellis Holbrook,
Harvey Jennings,
Edward Lewis."

22

I will lead them in paths that they have not known.

"SEE here, Tip," called Mr. Minturn, appearing in his store door one morning not long after the examination; "I want to talk to you."

Tip swung his basket off his shoulder and went into the store. He was at work for Mr. Dewey, and every piece of meat which he carried home took the form, in his eyes, of a Latin grammar and a dictionary; for these two books were what he was at present aiming after.

"I'm in a great hurry, Mr. Minturn," he said; "I've got a piece of meat for your folks in my basket, and I expect they want it."

"They'll have to wait till they get it," answered Mr. Minturn; "but I never hinder folks long. What are you going to do with yourself, now school's out?"

"Oh, work; anything I can find to do while vacation lasts."

"So you're going to keep on at school, are you? I thought likely, since your father was laid up, you'd be hunting for steady work so you could help the family along. There's a hard winter coming, you know."

There was no mistaking Mr. Minturn's tone. It said, as plainly as words could have done, "That's what I think you ought to do, anyhow."

Tip looked troubled. "There's nothing for me to do," he said at last; "I don't know of a place in this town where I could get steady work that I could do; and besides, if there was, I'm after an education now."

"My brother is here from Albany," Mr. Minturn made answer to this. "He is a merchant, has a large store there, and keeps a great many clerks. He's been plagued to death lately with one of his boys; when he sent him home with bundles, he'd open them and help himself; and my brother told me last night if I could warrant him a boy who was perfectly honest, he'd take him home with him, pay his fare down, and do well by him. I thought of you right away, and I told my brother that you were just the boy for him; you'd be as true as steel; but then, if you're going to keep on at school, it's all up."

Mr. Minturn did not add that he had kept his brother until eleven o'clock the night before, telling him Tip's history; what a boy he had been, how he had changed, how he was struggling upward; and, finally, the whole story of the examination—the failure, the downfall, the public confession—nor how his brother had listened eagerly and had said with energy, after the story was finished:

"Such a boy as that ought to be helped; and I'm ready to help him."

None of this did Tip hear, but he stooped down for his basket when Mr. Minturn had finished speaking with a bright blush on his cheek; it was something for a boy like him to be called "as true as steel."

"Yes," he said decidedly; "I'm going to keep on at school, that's certain; thank you all the same."

And out he went; yet all the way up and down the streets his thoughts were busy over what he had just heard. It was *time* certainly, as poor as they were, that he began to work; his mother's sewing supported the family now, and hard and late into the nights she had to work to keep them from hunger. Tip had thought of this question before, but had always comforted himself with the thought that work was not by any means an easy thing to get in the village, the odd jobs which he could find, out of school hours, being really the only things he could get to do. But no such comfort came to him today; here was a chance, and a splendid one, for getting steady work and, by and by, good wages probably. Why wasn't he glad?

Oh, ever since he gave himself to Christ, there had been in his heart a longing to get an education, and not only that, but to become a minister. Very small, faint hopes he had, and even those were brightened sometimes at their own boldness; but every day the desire grew stronger; and it did not seem as though he could possible give up school now. It was out of the question, he told himself, just as he was beginning to enjoy his books so much and was doing well. Mr. Burrows would be disappointed in him; he had encouraged him to study. No, it couldn't be done. He would consider the matter settled. And yet there was his mother, working day and night, and he, her only son, was not helping. There was his father, growing weaker every day, coughing harder every night; long ago they had given up the hope that the cough would ever leave him. There was Kitty, who ought to be in school but could not because her mother *must* have the little help which she could give. Tip was half distracted with thinking about it; he felt provoked at Mr. Minturn and Mr. Minturn's brother and the store in Albany and the boy who helped himself out of other people's bundles; they were all trying to cheat him out of his education. A dozen times he said it was settled, and as many times began at the beginning to think it all over again. He went home finally, after the meat was carried around; but this didn't help him any. Home hadn't gone back to its old state of dirt and disorder; Kitty's first attempt had been too successful, and she had liked the looks of things too well to give up; so there was a great change for the better in the housekeeping, which both Kitty and her mother enjoyed; still there was no denying that, though clean, it was a very forlorn little room, with very few things for comfort or convenience. Tip had never seen this with such wide-open eyes as he did today; so coming home did not quiet the vexing thoughts.

He split wood and pumped water without whistling a note, growing more sober every minute. At last, after supper, when the work was all done that he could do, he drew a sigh of relief; it was so nice to have time for thought; he could go up to his attic, and he would not come down, no, not if it wasn't in three days, until this thing was decided finally and forever.

Kitty sewed steadily on the seam which her mother had fixed for her and wondered why Tip didn't come down and hear her lesson, which had been ready for him this hour. It was another hour before he came; then his mother said:

"Tip, if you've a cent in the world, do take it and go and get your father some of that cough candy. I do believe he hasn't stopped coughing since supper."

Tip took his hat and started for the store; as he went he whistled a little. The cough candy was found at a store away uptown, and, getting a paper out of it, Tip dashed on around the corner and opened Mr. Minturn's store door.

"When is your brother going home?" he asked without ceremony, seeing Mr. Minturn behind the counter.

"Next Monday."

"Well, I'm going to talk to Father, and I think likely I'll want to go along with him."

"All right."

So Tip slammed the door and ran away, and Mr. Minturn never knew what a downfall that decision had been to the boy's dear hopes and plans.

It was all settled in the course of a day or two. Mr. Minturn, from Albany, was very kind. Tip was to have wages that seemed a small fortune to him, and enough had been advanced to get him a new suit of clothes, which his mother made.

One would have supposed that the future would look bright to him; yet it was with a very sad heart that he took his seat in prayer meeting that Thursday evening, the last time he expected to be in that room for—he didn't know how long. He had a feeling that he ought to be very glad and thankful, and wasn't at all.

Through the opening hymns and prayers his heart kept growing heavier every moment, and it was not until Mr. Holbrook arose and repeated the text which he had chosen for the evening that Tip could arouse himself to listen. It was a queer text, so he thought: "Who shall roll away the stone?" What could Mr. Holbrook be going to say on that? He found out and had reason to remember it forever after. As he went out from that meeting his thoughts, had he spoken them, would have been like these:

"That's true—I don't believe any man but Mr. Holbrook would ever have thought of it; they worried at a great rate about that stone, how they would get it rolled away, and when they got there it was gone. I'll remember that; I'll do just as I said; when I see a stone ahead of me I won't stop and fret about it; I'll walk straight up to it, and when I get there maybe it will roll out of my way."

23

*A word fitly spoken is like apples of gold
in pictures of silver.*

BEHOLD Tip, now in Albany, far away from home
and friends, from everyone that he had ever seen
before, save Mr. Howard Minturn, young Howard's
uncle.

But he had been there some time and was growing
into a settled-at-home feeling. It had been a wonderful change to him. Mr. Minturn did not board his
clerks; but for some reason, best known to himself, he
had taken Tip home with him. For a few days the boy
felt as though the roses on the carpets were made of
glass and would smash if he stepped on them. But he
was getting used to it all; he could sit squarely on his
chair at the table instead of on the edge, spread his
napkin over his lap as the others did, and eat his pie
with a silver fork under the light of the sparkling gas.

"Mother," said little Alice Minturn, "why does
Father have Edward board here and sit at the table
with us?"

"Because, Alice, your father wants to help him in
every way; your uncle Minturn thinks he is an unusually good, smart boy."

"I think so, too," said Alice, and was satisfied.

And Tip Lewis was Tip no longer; no one knew him by that name; everyone there said "Edward," save the store clerks, and they called him "Ed."

He had a queer feeling sometimes that he was somebody else and that Tip Lewis, whom he used to know so well, would be very much astonished if he could see him now.

He went into Sabbath school and became a member of Mr. Minturn's Bible class; but teachers were scarce, and before he had been there three weeks Mr. Minturn sent him to take charge of a class of very little boys who called him "Mr. Lewis" and made him feel strange and tall; he began to realize that he was almost sixteen years old and growing very fast.

He was leading a very busy life nowadays: at work all day in and for the store, and in the evening doing all he could with his books. Those books and his love for them were a great safeguard to him, kept him away from many a temptation to go astray; and yet it was hard work to accomplish much in the little time he had, and with no helper. Sometimes he sighed wearily and felt as though the road was full of stones.

"I pity you, old fellow," one of the younger clerks said to him one evening as they were leaving the store.

"I don't know for what?" was the good-natured answer.

"Why, Mr. Minturn's pink of a perfect and wonderful and altogether amazing son Ray has just got home from the university; saw him pass the store not an hour ago, leaning back in the carriage like a prince."

"What's he?" asked Edward.

"He's a prig; that's what he is."

"What's a prig?"

"Ho! you're a greeney, if you don't know what a prig is—wait till he snubs you and lords it over you awhile; then I guess you'll know. He'll have a good chance, seeing you're right there at the house all the while. I wouldn't be in your shoes for a penny."

In spite of its making him a great greeney, Edward did not know what a prig was; but judging from his companion's tone, he decided that it must be something very disagreeable. He went home feeling cross and uncomfortable, wishing that Ray were anybody in the world rather than Mr. Minturn's son, or anywhere else rather than at home. He was beginning to have such a nice time there; they were all so kind to him and really seemed to like him; it was too bad to have it all spoiled.

"I know what kind of a fellow he is," he muttered to himself; "he's like that Mr. Symonds who comes to the store twice a week or so after kid gloves and acts as if he thought he was a great deal too good to ask me a decent question. My! I wish he was in Texas."

The dining room was a blaze of light when he peeped in; soon after, the family were gathered, waiting for Mr. Minturn; the newcomer sat on the sofa, one arm around little Alice and the other resting gently on his mother's lap. Edward guessed, by his mother's face, that she did *not* wish he was in Texas. Mr. Minturn came in presently, and Edward stole into the room just behind him; but Alice called him eagerly:

"Edward, Ray has come! Come over here and see him."

"Go ahead," said Mr. Minturn, as Edward stood still, with very red cheeks; and Ray sat up and held out his hand.

"How do you do, Edward? Alice has been making me acquainted with you this afternoon, so you're not a stranger."

How very clear and kind his tones were! Edward was astonished. That same evening he was more astonished. He was in the library at work over his books; Mr. Minturn had had to go to a committee meeting, expecting to be detained late; as he arose from the dinner table, he had said:

"How am I to get in tonight? Here's my night key in two pieces."

"I'll be night key, sir," said Edward promptly.

"Well, you may; you can take your books to the library and have a long evening to pore over them."

So he was there, poring over them with all his might, when the door opened gently and Ray Minturn came in.

"Are you hard at work?" he asked kindly.

"Yes, sir," said Edward, wishing he would go out again. But he didn't seem in a hurry to do so; he took a book from the case and glanced over it a moment, then came toward Edward.

"What are you studying?"

"Fractions," answered Edward briefly.

"Do you have any trouble?"

"Yes, lots," speaking a little crossly, for he wanted to go on with his work. "I can't get this one I'm at to save my head."

"Suppose I see what is the matter?" And Ray drew a chair to the table, and sat down, glancing his eye over the slate.

"Rather, suppose you see for yourself," he said in a few moments. "Just run over that multiplication at the top of the slate."

"Oh, bother!" Edward said after he had obeyed orders; "that figure three has made me all this trouble."

"Smaller things than figure threes make trouble. Have you been to school lately?"

"Always, till I came here; but I might just as well have been out last winter."

"What happened last winter?"

"Lots of things," answered Edward, with brightening eyes. But he didn't seem disposed to state any of them; so, after waiting a little, Ray asked, "Wouldn't you get on faster with your books if you had a teacher?"

"Think likely I should; but I haven't got any, so I'll have to get on as fast as I can."

"How would it do if I should play teacher while I am at home and give you the hour from nine till ten?"

Edward laid down his pencil, turned his eyes for the first time full upon Ray, and looked at him in utter astonishment.

"Do you mean it?" he asked at last.

"Certainly, I do; I shouldn't say so if I didn't. Don't you think you would like it?"

"Like it! I guess I would. But I don't know— What do you do it for?"

"Because I am glad to help a boy who seems to be trying to help himself; we will consider it settled, then. It is ten o'clock; will you come out to prayers now?"

And at this the astonished look on Edward's face deepened.

"Is Mr. Minturn here?" he asked.

"No, but his son is. Are you so surprised that I should have prayers in my father's absence?"

"Yes," said Edward; "I didn't know—I mean, I didn't think—"

"You didn't think I had learned to pray, perhaps. Thank God, I have." Then he laid his hand kindly on

Edward's shoulder. "Have *you* learned that precious lesson yet, my friend?"

"Yes," said Edward softly; "a good while ago."

"I am very glad; you will never learn anything else that is quite so important. What is all this study for, by the way? Have you any plans?"

"Yes," said Edward, astonished at what he was about to tell to a stranger; "I want to get an education, and then, if I possibly *can* do that, I want to be a minister."

Ray's hand fell from his shoulder, and when he answered this, his voice was low and a little sad.

"God bless you and help you. I hope you will never have to give it up."

Edward made up his mind that night that a prig meant the best and kindest—yes, and the wisest, young man in the world.

24

Whatsoever ye would that men should do to you,
do ye even so to them.

THE LONG, bright summer days and the glowing autumn days were gone; midwinter was upon them. During all this time Edward was hard at work; there was plenty of business to be done at the store. He had been promoted; very rarely, nowadays, was he called on to carry home purchases or to do errands. He had his counter and his favorite customers. There had been another change, too, which Edward felt sure Ray had had a hand in; Ray had a hand in everything that was good and thoughtful. He had long evenings for study now; he came up to dinner with Mr. Minturn at six o'clock and had no further work to do until the next day. Oh, those long evenings! What rapid progress he made; what a teacher Ray was! Could a boy help getting on who was so carefully and kindly led?

What was *not* Ray to him? Teacher, friend, brother; constant, unfailing, loving guide. Edward was learning to love him with an almost worship.

Meantime, everyone saw better than did Edward himself how he had changed. He had not been in constant intercourse with a Christian family, who lived their religion every day and every hour, for nothing; his improvement had been constant and rapid.

He came home from the post office one evening with his hands full of letters, among them a very queer-looking one for himself. He carried the others to the library, and his own to his room. Such an odd letter as it was! He was glad it was his business to get the mail, and that none of the other clerks had seen this with his name written at the very top of the envelope, and written "Tip" at that. How odd it looked; and how queer it sounded when he said it over! It was so long since he had heard that name; he never wanted to again. He was glad that Ray Minturn had never called him Tip, nor heard him called so.

Who could it be from? Nobody wrote to him except Kitty, and once in a long while his mother; but this was no home letter. At last he broke the seal and read:

> "Deer Tip, *Mother's dead, I feel bad, you kno that, so what's the use? I've got to go to work. I like you better than any of the other felows, always did. Can't I com out there to your store and work, I'll behave myself reel wel; I will, honor bright, if you'll git me a place. I've got money enuff to get there. I dug potatoes for old Williams and earned it. Rite to me rite off that's a good fellow. I want to com awful,*
> "Bob Turner."

Edward was thunderstruck! He dropped the letter on the floor in disgust. What was to be done now? The idea of having Bob Turner there was perfectly dreadful; besides, thank fortune, it was impossible; they wanted more help, to be sure, had been looking out for a boy that very day, but not such a one as Bob—that was out of the question. And yet—Bob's mother was dead! In his rude, careless way, Bob had loved his mother rather better than he had anyone else; and Edward did not doubt that he felt bad. He was without friends now; surely he needed one if he ever did. But it was *so* disagreeable to think of having him there—he was so different from any of the others, and he would call *him* Tip, and be always around in his way; would seem to lead him back to the old life from which he thought he had escaped altogether. It was not to be thought of for a moment. But then—and now came a startling thought. How long he had been praying for Bob! Perhaps this was the way in which God meant to answer, by giving him a chance to work as well as pray. Perhaps he ought to be *willing* to have him come. No matter how much the clerks might make fun of him for having such a friend; no matter how much pain and annoyance it might cause him; if this was God speaking to him to help his brother, how dreadful it would be to make no answer!

He sat down to think about it; his algebra lay open before him; he was not quite ready for Ray, but he could not attend to algebra now.

"Let me see," he said; "if there *should* be such a thing as that Bob could come, what would I do for him? One of two things is certain. Either he'll lead me or I shall him; we always did when we were together much. Which will it be? If he leads me, he'll lead me into mischief, just as sure as the world; if I lead *him,* I'll try to keep him out of mischief. It's clear that I ought to be the leader. Now, how would I do it, I wonder? Bob ought to be a Christian; he won't be safe two minutes at a time until he is. If God says anything, he says he'll hear prayer. If I believe that, why don't I pray for Bob, so that he'll be converted? I *do* pray for him always, but it's kind of halfway praying—kind of as if I thought it was a pretty hard thing for God to do after all. That's wrong. God wants him safe, and he knows he isn't safe now, and he's willing to help him; it must be my fault that he don't. My business and lessons, and all that sort of thing, are putting Bob and Ellis, and even Father, pretty much out of my thoughts. That's wrong too, and must be stopped. Mr. Minturn says a thing is never half done that hasn't a corner in the day belonging to itself. I'll try that rule. After this, every evening at half past eight I'll come up here to my room and lock the door, and I'll pray for Bob; I'll pray as though I expected an answer and was going to be on the lookout for it. I won't let anything hinder me from coming at just that time, unless it's something that I can't help. Meantime, I'll get him a place if I can."

Edward was straightforward as Tip had been; this point decided, he went downstairs to the library door and knocked.

Mr. Minturn was alone and busy; but he looked up as Edward entered in answer to his "Come in."

"Well, sir; what is it?"

"Have you time for a little piece of business?"

"Always time for business; sit down. What is it about?"

"Have you found a boy yet?"

"No. Have you?"

"Yes, sir, there's a boy out home who wants to come; I've just had a letter from him; his name is Turner—Bob Turner."

"Is he a good boy?"

"No, sir."

"Well! that's plain; what are you talking about, then?"

"I want you to make him a good boy, sir."

"Humph! That's an idea. I can't make boys over new; is he honest?"

"No, sir, I don't think he is very; not what you mean by honest; but his mother is dead, and he hasn't any friends; he goes with a miserable set of fellows, and he'll get worse than he is in no time if he stays there."

"And the whole of it is, you think it's my duty to let him come and try to save him! Suppose I should, what would you do for your share?"

"I'd try, too."

"How?"

"Why, I'd try to get him to do right."

"Suppose he should try to get you to do wrong?"

"He couldn't!" said Edward positively.

"How did you find that out?"

"Because I should pray for myself every day, and for Bob too; and God hears prayer."

"Yes, but God's people sometimes get very far away from him; if this Bob should lead *you* astray, I'd be sorry I ever heard of him."

"I don't feel much afraid," Edward said, speaking this time in a more quiet, less positive tone, "for I never go wrong when I pray often; pray about everything that comes up, you know, and mean what I pray for."

"Humph," said Mr. Minturn, "that's a good idea; I guess you're pretty safe under *that* rule."

"Besides," said Edward, reserving one of his best arguments till the last, "I know somebody who would help Bob ever so much—Mr. Ray would find him out."

Mr. Minturn's eyes grew bright, and he smiled a half-sad smile.

"Yes," he said, "that's true enough; Ray can't come near anybody without helping him. Well, write to the boy to come on; we'll try him; has he anything to come with?"

"Yes, sir, he says he has money enough to get here." And Edward went away glad, for he had begun to be very willing to have Bob there.

25

If ye abide in me, and my words abide in you, ye shall ask what ye will, and it shall be done unto you.

EDWARD got up one morning feeling years older than he had only the morning before—older and graver—feeling a great responsibility resting on his shoulders; for he was fatherless! The weary frame, racked with so many pains, was at last at rest. Kitty had written just a line, telling the sad story, but it did not reach him until nearly a week after; and with it came Mr. Holbrook's—a long letter, full of tender sympathy, telling all about how, in the afternoon of an early spring day, they had laid his father by Johnny's side.

Edward read on eagerly, until he came to this sentence: "My dear boy, I have a most precious message for you; I was with him only an hour before he died, and at that time he said to me, 'I want you to tell Tip that God has heard his prayer and saved his father, and that I shall watch for him to come to heaven, and bring all the rest.' And, Edward, I haven't a shade of doubt but that your father is with his Redeemer; you must let me quote again a verse which I once gave you: 'I love the Lord, because he hath heard my voice and my supplications.'"

And at this point the letter dropped from his hand, and Edward shed his first tears for his father.

It was curious, the different ways that Mr. Minturn and his son had of expressing sympathy.

"Oh," Mr. Minturn said when he was told, "why in the world didn't they send for you?"

"Because, sir, my father died very suddenly, and my mother thought I could not afford to come so far for the funeral."

"Afford! As if that would have made any difference. Did they think I would let it cost *you* anything?"

Edward showed Mr. Holbrook's letter to Ray after that; and when it had been read, expressed the feeling which had been much in his heart ever since the news came and which had been strengthened by Mr. Minturn's words.

"I shall always be sorry that I could not have gone to the funeral."

And Ray answered, resting his arm, as he spoke, lightly on Edward's shoulder to express the tenderness which he felt; "No you won't, my dear fellow; when you get up there, in the glory of the Redeemer's presence, and meet your father face-to-face, you will not remember to be sorry that you did not see him *buried.*"

Meantime Bob had come and been set at work. He did not board at Mr. Minturn's. Edward had heard that matter arranged with a little sigh of relief; his precious hour with Ray, then, would be undisturbed.

Bob was doing very much better than anybody who knew him would have imagined he *could* do; he seemed to have made up his mind to behave himself, sure enough. Yet his being there was a trial to Edward in several ways—he had a great horror of being called "Tip"; that name belonged to the miserable, ragged, friendless, hopeless boy who used to wander around the streets in search of mischief, not to the young man who was a faithful clerk in one of the finest stores in Albany, besides being a teacher in Sabbath school and a very fair scholar in Latin and algebra. But Bob Turner could not be made to understand all this; and though he stared at the neat black suit which Edward wore, and opened his eyes wide when Mr. Minturn went and came in company with his old companion and honored him in many ways, he still called him "Tip," in clear, round tones that rang through the store a dozen times a day. But there was nothing which Ray could not smooth over, so Edward thought, when one evening he flounced into the library with a very much disturbed face.

"I wish that fellow knew anything," he said angrily.

"What is the matter now?" Ray asked, meeting the bright, angry eyes with a quiet smile.

Edward laughed a little. "Well, I can't help feeling vexed; Bob screeches that hateful little name after me wherever I go. I despise that name, and I wish he could be made to understand it."

"How did you happen to be called Tip at first?"

"Why," said Edward, turning over the leaves of his dictionary, "my little sister Kitty made it up before she could talk plain; how she ever got that name out of Edward, I don't know; I'm sure I wish she had been asleep when she did it; but that's what she called me, and that's what I've been ever since."

"And did Johnny, the little boy that died, ever call you so?"

Edward's eyes began to grow soft.

"Often," he said gently; "and it was about the only name he could speak; he was a little fellow."

"Well, Edward, I should not think it would be such

a very disagreeable name to you, when your father, who is gone, always used it, and always in kindness, you told me; and it is the only name by which little Johnny can remember you. There are two things to be thought of in this matter," Ray continued after a moment, finding Edward not disposed to speak; "one is, if you hope to do anything with this old companion of yours, you must be ready to take worse things from him than a quiet, inoffensive little name like that; he will learn your right name, perhaps, in time. And the other is, What is Bob Turner's right name, my friend?"

Edward's face flushed, his lips quivered into a little smile, then he laughed outright.

"It would be ridiculous to call *him* Robert!" he said, still laughing. "Ray, here's my exercise, if you want it now."

And Ray heard no more complaints about the offending little name.

"Say, Tip, just go home with me tonight?" Bob coaxed one evening, as Edward, having been detained late at the store, was leaving just as Bob was closing the shutters. "Mr. Ray's head is so bad you won't have any plaguey lessons tonight to hinder you. Every single fellow in the store but me is going to the theater, and I am awful lonesome up there alone."

"It is a wonder you are not going, too," said Edward.

"No, it ain't. I can keep a promise once in a while, I reckon. That Ray Minturn can do anything with a fellow, and I was fool enough to promise him that I wouldn't go. Come, go up home with me; do, that's a good fellow."

"No," said Edward decidedly, "I can't."

"Now, Tip Lewis, I think you're real mean; you don't never come to see me no more than if I was in Guinea. You act as if you were ashamed of me, and I keep my word and behave myself, too; and you're a mean, chicken-hearted fellow, if you're ashamed to notice me nowadays, just because you board in a big house and dress like a dandy."

"Poh!" said Edward, "what nonsense that is! I'd look well being ashamed of anyone that Minturn talked with; but, Bob, I can't go tonight, nor any other night just about this time because I made a promise that I'd do something else at exactly half past eight, and that nothing in the world should hinder me if I could help it; and it can't be far from half past eight now."

Bob eyed him curiously. "Tip, you're the oddest fellow born, I do believe," he said at last. "Is it lessons?"

"No; it's nothing about lessons."

"Couldn't I *help* you do it?"

"Yes," said Edward, after a thoughtful silence; "you *could* help me better than anyone else, only you won't."

"Well, now," Bob answered earnestly, "as sure as I'm alive I will, if you'll tell me what it is; I'll help you this very night."

"Do you promise?" asked Edward.

"Yes I do, out and out; and when I promise a thing through and through, why *you* know, Tip Lewis, that I do it."

"Well," said Edward, as he tried the door to see that all was safe before leaving; "then I'll tell you. Every night, at exactly half past eight, I go to my room and ask God over and over again to make you want to be a Christian."

Not a single word did Bob answer to this; he took long strides up the street by the side of Edward in the direction of Mr. Minturn's, never once speaking until they had reached the door and stood waiting to be let in; then he said, "Tip, that's mean."

"What is?"

"To get a fellow to promise what he can't do."

"I have not. Don't you want to be a Christian?"

"No; I can't say that I'm particular about it."

"But that's too silly to believe; you need a friend to help you about as badly as anyone I know of, and when you can have one for the asking, why shouldn't you want him? Besides, I didn't say *make* you a Christian, anyhow; I said make you *want* to be one. You can pray *that,* I'm sure; anyway, you promised, and I trusted you."

Bob followed him through the hall, up the stairs, to his neat little room, and whistled "Hail Columbia" while he lighted a match and turned on the gas.

"My! you have things in style here, don't you?" he said, looking around while the bright light gleamed over the pretty carpet and shining furniture.

"Yes," said Edward; "everything in this house is in style. Bob, it's half past eight."

"Well," Bob said good-naturedly, "I'd like to know what I'm to do; this is new business to me, you see."

"I'm going to kneel down here and pray for you, and you promised to do the same."

Edward knelt at his bedside, and Bob, half laughing, followed his example. But Christ must have been praying too, and putting words into Edward's heart to say. By and by, in spite of himself, Bob had to put up his hand and dash away a tear or two. He had never heard himself prayed for before.

That evening was one to be remembered by Bob Turner, for more than one reason. Ray sent for both of the boys to come to his room; he was sick, but not too sick to see and talk with Bob whenever he could get a chance. He made the half hour spent with him so pleasant that Bob gave an eager assent to the request that he would come often. More than that, he kept his word; and as often as he passed Edward's door toward nine o'clock, he stepped lightly, for he knew that he was being prayed for, and there began to come into his heart a strange longing to pray for himself. One evening he discovered that Ray, too, prayed every night for him, and the vague notion grew into a certainty that what they two were so anxious about for him, he ought to desire for himself.

"Ye shall ask what ye will, and it shall be done unto you."

Edward had taken this promise into his heart; he was trying to live up to the condition to abide in Christ, and in due season God made his promise sure.

"I wish," Bob said to Ray one evening, when the weary head was full of pain, "I *do* wish I could do something for you."

"You can," Ray answered quickly; "something that I would like better than almost anything else in the world."

"What is it?" Bob's question was sincere and eager.

"Give yourself to Christ."

Bob heard this in grave, earnest silence.

"I would," he said after a minute, "if I knew how."

"Do you mean that?"

"Yes, I do; I'm sick of waiting, and I'm sick of myself."

"If I should tell you how, would you do it?"

"Yes, I would," spoken, evidently, with honest meaning.

"Kneel down, then, here beside me, and say to God that you want to be a Christian; that you are willing to give yourself up to him now and forever, to do just as he tells you."

Bob hesitated, struggling a little, and at last knelt down. There was silence in the room while three sincere hearts were lifted up in prayer; and, surely, Christ bent low to listen. When Bob would have risen, Ray laid one hand on his arm and, steadying his throbbing head with the other, said solemnly:

"Blessed Redeemer, here is a soul given up to thee. Do thou take it, and wash it in thy precious blood, and make it fit for heaven. We ask boldly, because thou hast promised and we know that thy promises are sure."

"Edward," Ray said the next evening as they sat alone and were silent for a little, after Bob had left them and gone home rejoicing in the hope of sins washed away, "what was that verse that your minister at home quoted for you in his letter?"

"'I love the Lord, because he hath heard my voice and my supplications.'" Edward repeated it with brightening eyes.

26

*And when they looked, they saw that the stone
was rolled away.*

ONWARD sped the busy days, until at last there came
an evening which made it exactly three years since
Edward had first set foot in Albany. They had been years
of wonderful progress to him. He had gone on steadily
with his evening studies; he had been an eager pupil,
and Ray had been a faithful teacher. This evening he sat
in the library waiting for Ray, but he had a very
troubled face. Once more he took Kitty's long letter out
of his pocket. Kitty wrote long letters once in two
weeks, but it was a rare thing to have a postscript added
by his mother. He turned to this and read it again; it was
a very kind one. They were doing well now, so she
wrote; her health was very good now that she slept
quietly at night—and just here Edward knew there had
come in a heavy sigh—because there was no constant
coughing to disturb her rest. She had steady work and
could support Kitty and herself nicely without his help;
he must keep what he earned for himself after this.
"Kitty says you want to go to school," so the letter ran;
"if you do, save up your money for that. Your poor father
had a notion that you would make a scholar; I think it
would please him if you did."

Surely he could not wish for a kinder, more thoughtful letter than this; coming from his *mother*, too! She must have changed much, as well as himself. But this very letter had greatly unsettled his quiet life—the old longing to give himself up to study, to prepare for the ministry, had broken loose and well-nigh overwhelmed him with its power. He wanted it, oh, so much; it had grown strong, instead of weak, during these three years. But what to do, and how to do it? That was the question. Certainly, he was not prepared to answer it. If he stayed where he was, led his busy life all day in the store, how was he ever to go through with the necessary course of study, which it was high time he commenced in earnest? If he left them, these dear friends who had taken him into their home and hearts, and made him feel like one of them, how was he to live while he studied? How, indeed, could he study at all? The truth was, Edward, calling to mind Mr. Holbrook's lecture that last evening in the home prayer meeting, and his resolution taken then, thought that the stone was ahead of him no longer, but that he had walked *close* up to it and could not take another step because of it, and very large and impossible to move did it look to his shortsighted eyes.

Just as he was growing hopelessly moody, Ray came in and settled himself among the cushions, rather wearily.

"Ray," said Edward anxiously, "you are not well enough for lessons tonight."

"No," answered Ray, smiling, however, as he spoke, "I think I am not, because I want to talk instead. I am full of a scheme which needs your help; for once, we'll let the lessons go. It is an age since I have heard anything concerning your plans; you have not given up your desire for the ministry, I hope?"

"No, Ray; I shall never give that up."

"I thought not; it would not be like you. That being the case, isn't it time to do something definite?"

"Time, certainly," Edward answered gloomily; "but what's to do?"

"That brings me to the unfolding of my scheme. Edward, do you know that it was my lifelong desire to reach the point toward which you are looking?"

"No," said Edward with pitying interest; "I never thought of it."

"Well," and Ray smiled sadly, "it is so; and I hope you may never know how hard it is to have to give up such a wish. I cannot say that I did actually give it up entirely until very lately. I gave up all study three years ago and came home to regain strength; *you* know how well I have succeeded in that." And Ray pressed his thin, wasting hand across his damp forehead. "It is all over now, *utterly.*" The hand did duty now for a moment, shading his eyes from the light. Presently he spoke more cheerily: "All over for myself, but not for you; so, Edward, what I want to say tonight, in brief, is this: you have talents, perseverance, and health; I have money—the four combined cannot fail to speed you in your work. What say you?"

"I—I don't understand you," Edward spoke in complete bewilderment.

"Let me speak more plainly. I want you to go now, *immediately,* to some good preparatory school, thence to college, thence to the seminary, and the means wherewith to do these three important things shall be at your disposal. Isn't that plain?"

"Why," said Edward, "I don't know what to say; I am too much astonished, and—and thankful."

"Then you will do it?"

"Only—Ray?"

"Well?"

"Isn't there a right kind of pride about being helped in these things?"

"There is a great deal of wrong kind of pride. Let me show you," and he sat up and spoke eagerly. "It is right and honorable for people to help themselves in this world, but very vain and foolish to refuse help which would greatly aid the cause that they profess to have at heart. You see how it is; God has given me money; I am ready and waiting to give it back to him. I would gladly give myself to him in the ministry; I have longed and prayed for this; but he has seen fit not to answer as I wished. I have no strength to give; you have and are ready to give it. Do you think God would be less pleased with the offering if we united it, thus giving me a chance to do something?"

"No," said Edward, speaking very slowly, "only, I had hoped to accomplish my plans without help from anyone but God."

Ray leaned back again, among the cushions, and spoke wearily:

"That is, you prefer to be a great many years longer in preparation than you need be and have about half as much strength, finally, as you would have had you not overworked, rather than give me a chance to do what I could since I cannot do what I would."

"But, Ray, there are plenty of people to help, even if you do no more for me. The world is full of poor young men, struggling to get an education."

"Yes, that is so; and I suppose you would enjoy helping some young man out in Oregon, of whom you had never heard, quite as well as you would me."

Edward came quickly to the sofa, where Ray was lying, and laid his hand tenderly over the closed eyes.

"Ray, there is nothing in the world I would not do for you."

"Will you let me help you into the ministry, as rapidly as money *can* help?"

"I will be glad to; it is a great, noble offer, and I thank you from my heart. You mustn't think that I don't; only I thought—perhaps—"

"I know," said Ray, for Edward had stopped doubtfully; "I understand just how you feel; but I *do* think the feeling, in this case, at least, is wrong; and, my dear brother, you will be glad when you know how thankful you have made me."

"Yes; and after all you will not be doing any more for me—you *can't*—than you have done. I think money is very little, compared with that. Ray," and Edward sank down among the cushions in front of him, "I do believe you are more to me than any other human being ever will be."

Ray smiled, quite as if he did not think so, but would not unsay it for anything.

"It is all right," he said gently, after a little silence. "I think you will do so much more than I ever *could* have done. God bless you, my dear brother."

After that Edward went up to his room, got out his little red Bible, his precious lamp, and opening to the history of the rockbound grave, read on until he came to the verse, "And when they looked, they saw that the stone was rolled away." Around this he made heavy marks with his pencil, thinking, meantime, that the angel of the Lord was still at work on earth.

"Bob," said Edward, stopping before Bob's counter two days after this matter was settled, "I am going to start for home in the morning."

"Are you, though?" Bob answered eagerly, stopping

his work to take the sentence in fully. "My! I wish I was going along, just to see what folks would say."

"About *you*, do you mean?" said Edward, laughing, and thinking wonderingly, as well as joyfully, of the change which there had been in Bob Turner.

Bob had a counter, too, and was no longer an errand boy; there had very rarely been known such a rapid promotion in that store; but the truth was, Mr. Minturn had early learned that Bob Turner was destined to be, not a minister, nor a lawyer, not even a scholar, but a thorough, energetic, successful merchant. He had no sooner made this discovery than he determined to give the boy a chance.

So Bob had earned a name and a place in the store, and was a general favorite with the other clerks, and was beginning to have customers who sought him out and liked to make purchases of him. More than all, Bob was an earnest Christian; his loving tenderness for, and almost worship of, Ray Minturn kept him from being much led into temptation, and his influence over the younger clerks was growing to be for good. He was destined to be more popular than Edward had been; for Edward had risen too rapidly, and was too much at home with the entire Minturn family not to be looked upon with some degree of envy.

"Well, Tip—" Bob had never learned not to say Tip and probably never would, but Edward had long since forgotten to care—"tell everyone at home that I'm well and happy, and never want to see one of them again. I don't believe I have a friend there: anyhow, I know I don't deserve to have."

27

Wherewithal shall a young man cleanse his way?
by taking heed thereto according to thy word.

KITTY Lewis shook out the folds of her new, bright pink calico dress, walked to the little looking glass for about the tenth time to see if the dainty white ruffle around her neck was in order, then took a survey of the room, lest there might possibly be something else to do which would improve its appearance.

It was the same little room in which Kitty had spent her childhood, from which Johnny first, and then long afterwards the husband and father, had been carried out to return no more. And yet it was *not* the same—there was a neat rag carpet on the floor, a Christmas gift from Mrs. Minturn; the round table in the corner was covered with a bright red cloth and strewn with a few books and papers; the full, white curtain was looped away from the window, and the light of a clear sunset glimmered in the room; everything was neat and bright and cheery. The table was set for tea, the white cloth showing just the folds in which it was ironed; there were three plates and three cups and saucers instead of two, while Kitty, in her restless wanderings around the room, and Mrs. Lewis, in her frequent glances out of the window, both showed that somebody was being watched and waited for.

"The eastern train is in," Kitty said finally. "Now, if he comes tonight he'll be here in three minutes." And it could not have been much more than that when a quick, crushing step was heard on the gravel outside, then on the plank before the door, then the door swung open, and Edward Lewis walked into the little room out of which he had gone three years before.

Kitty was all ready to spring forward, say, "Oh, Tip," and throw her arms right around his neck. Instead, she stood still. Some way, in spite of the long letters which had passed between them during these years, Kitty had fully expected to see a stout, tanned boy in a strong, coarse suit of gray, with thick boots and a new straw hat. Or, at least—why, of course, she knew he must have changed some; hadn't she? But then she did *not* think he would be so tall and have a face and hands without tan or freckle, or that his clothes would be so *very* black and fine, and fit as though they had grown on him, or that his collar would be white and glossy or his boots so small and shiny. So Kitty stood still in embarrassed silence. But the mother, oh, she saw in him the picture of the dear, dead father, as he used to come to her long, long ago; the husband who, through all change and poverty and pain, she had *always* loved! And all the tenderness that had ever been in her heart took form and spoke in those words with which she came forward to greet her son—"Oh, my *dear* boy!"

There was happiness in the little home that night, only the bedroom door was closed, and Edward knew that his father's bed was vacant.

Such a queer feeling as possessed him all the next day, while he went around the village! He went *every*where. He felt like walking through every street and stepping on every stone on which his feet had trod in the old life—now utterly gone from him. He wandered down to the riverbank, where he had lain that summer morning and envied the fishes; and, standing there, thanked God for the mission class in Mr. Holbrook's Sabbath school. Thence to the cemetery, where by the side of little Johnny's grave the new life had been commenced. There was a long grave beside the short one now; and standing there, he thanked God for the hope which he had of meeting the father and the baby in heaven. Thence to the great elm tree at the foot of the hill; and standing there he took out once more the little red Bible and turned the leaves lovingly; lingered over the name written by Mr. Holbrook's hand, turned again to the first verse which he had ever read from its pages: "Thy word is a lamp unto my feet, and a light unto my path." Time and again had he proved the truth of that verse. There, under that very tree, it had helped him to fight battles with Satan and come off conqueror. And he thanked God for the Bible. After that he went directly to the village; just looked in at the meat market for the sake of the old days.

Somebody told Mr. Dewey who was coming, and he was just ready to say, "Hallo, Tip"; but instead, he came around from behind the counter and, holding out his hand, said, "How do you do, Lewis? Glad to see you."

Something, either in the city-made clothes or the quiet air of dignity with which they were worn, made him dislike to say, "Hallo, Tip," to the tall young man before him.

Mr. Minturn shook him heartily by the hand. "Never rejoiced over anyone's luck more in my life!" he said, then, in the same breath, "How's Ray? Oh yes,

I see how it is, poor fellow. And you love him too; of course, everyone does."

There was still the schoolroom to visit, and as Edward went up the familiar walk he wished Bob Turner could have been with him to make this call. But Bob was probably rushing like a top through the city store, without a thought of the old schoolhouse or the miserable days which he had spent there.

Mr. Burrows himself answered the knock and gave him a hearty greeting. Three years had made changes there. Edward found himself looking eagerly toward the back row of seats for the old faces—Will, Howard, Ellis, and half a dozen others—before he remembered that they had long since entered high schools. The boys whom he had left plodding through long division were filling those back seats now and leading their classes in algebra and Latin. He sat down near the blackboard to watch the progress of Joe Bartlett through an example in division. And behold, he was doing that old never-to-be-forgotten example about the cows and sheep! He picked up an arithmetic eagerly.

"Mr. Burrows, do you remember that example?"

"I remember that it has puzzled some forty or more of my boys in the course of time," said Mr. Burrows, laughing, "but nothing very special about it."

"I do; it was the cause of my first promotion."

"Was it, indeed! I'm afraid it will never be the cause of poor Joseph's; it seems to be mastering him."

Mr. Burrows was engaged with a grammar class, and Edward offered to assist the bewildered Joseph.

"I remember those sheep of old," he said kindly, as he turned to the board. "Isn't it the 'stood him in' that troubles you?"

"Yes, it is," Joe answered grumbly. "I don't see no sense to it."

"Let me show you. Suppose—" And he went through with the well-remembered explanation. It was successful; Joe understood it and went on briskly with his figures.

Edward turned toward Mr. Burrows. "It was the way my father explained it to me," he said with eyes that glistened a little.

Someone brought Mr. Burrows a note, and as he read and laid it down he said:

"Now, Edward, if you had continued at school instead of running away from us, I should get you to hear this recitation in algebra and take leave of absence for a few minutes. There is a friend in town whom I would give much to see before the next train leaves."

"Suppose you set me at it as it is."

Mr. Burrows looked surprised.

"Have you been studying algebra, Edward?"

"Somewhat."

"How far have you been?"

"Through."

"Do you feel *positive* that you could do examples over here?" turning to "Evolution."

"Entirely," Edward answered, smiling at Mr. Burrows's doubts. Ray had been a thorough teacher.

So Mr. Burrows went away, and Edward took his seat on the stage and commenced the recitation. At first the boys were disposed to be wise and display their knowledge; when they had known him last, he was in division. But he was in algebra now, or rather through it, and they speedily discovered that he seemed to have every example in the lesson committed to memory.

Meantime, Mr. Burrows returned and listened with astonishment and delight.

"Thank you heartily," he said afterwards; "you

ought to fit yourself for teaching. But, Edward, you did not get through algebra alone?"

"No," said Edward, flushing at the thought of Ray; "I had the best and wisest teacher on earth."

Well, he sat down in what had been his seat and tried to imagine that it was his seat still; that Bob would be in pretty soon and plague him while he studied his spelling lesson. But he could not do it. Things were different, very different. First and foremost, there was Ray; he had not known *him* in those days; if he had, he said to himself, things would have been different long before they were.

Going back uptown he met Mr. Holbrook, who turned and walked with him.

"And so," he said, after the long talk was concluded, "you go next week, do you?"

"Next Tuesday, sir."

"Well, God bless you, my friend, as he has, and will." Then, after a minute, "Edward, my son is a wanderer yet; do you still remember him?"

"Always, sir," Edward answered, in firm, steady tones; "and, Mr. Holbrook, God *never* forgets!"

As he went on past Mr. Minturn's store, could he have heard the remarks that were made there, very likely he might have remembered a certain statement which he had made to the little fishes that summer morning.

Mr. Minturn, looking out after him, said to Mr. Dewey:

"There goes one of the finest and most promising young men in this town."

"Yes," answered Mr. Dewey, laughing a little; "I used to notice that he improved every day after he brought back those circus tickets."

28

For thou shalt find it after many days.

"COME in," and the Rev. Edward Lewis laid down his book, pushed back his study chair, and was ready to receive whoever was knocking at his study door.

"Mr. Lewis," said the little girl who came in in answer to his invitation, "Father has just come from the post office, and he brought you some letters, and here they are."

Mr. Lewis thanked his little next-door neighbor, took his letters, and when the room was quiet again, settled back in his chair to enjoy them.

The first one was from a brother minister, begging an exchange. The next brought a look of surprise and delight to his face, for he recognized Ellis Holbrook's handwriting. And the delight spread and deepened as he read, especially when he came to one sentence: "I asked Father what message he had for you, and he replied, 'Send him this verse, and tell him that again it is peculiarly his: "I love the Lord, because he hath heard my voice and my supplications."'" That, you see, would have told me the whole story, without this long letter. I thank God that he put it into your heart to pray for me, as also that he has heard your prayers. God bless you. By the way, Father wants you to assist him on the first Sabbath in July. I earnestly hope you can do so; he thinks you will be coming east about that time."

Was there ever a more thankful heart than was that minister's as he laid down his old schoolfellow's letter? How constantly, how sometimes almost hopelessly, had he prayed for Ellis Holbrook! How many times had he been obliged to reassure himself with the promise, "In due season we shall reap, if we faint not." And now, again, had God's Word been verified to him. He took the letter up once more, to look lovingly at that closing, never before written by Ellis—"Your brother in Christ."

There was still another letter to read. That writing, too, was familiar; he had received many reminders of it during the past years. He laughed as he read, it sounded so like the writer:

"Albany, Jan. 18—

"Dear Tip, Do you have Fourth of July out your way this year? We do here in Albany; rather, I'm going to have one in my yard. Perhaps you remember a Fourth of July which you took me to once, when we were ragged little wretches at home? I do, anyhow, and this is to be twin-brother to that time. All the ugly, dingy little urchins that I know have been invited. We're to have fine fireworks and fine singing and fine *eating.* My wife added that last item; thought it a great improvement. I'm not sure but it is; most things are that she has a hand in. Now, to come to the point of this letter—you're going to make the speech on that occasion. No getting out of it now! I planned this thing one day in the old schoolhouse. Oh, did you know Mr. Burrows had given up teaching? Grown too old. Queer, isn't it? Don't seem as if anybody was growing old except me. At first I wasn't going to have my feast on the Fourth, because, you remember, it was on *that* day that our blessed Ray left us; but, talking with Mr. Minturn about it, he said Ray would have been delighted with it all, and so he would, you know. Don't think we are going to gather in all Albany; it's only the younger scholars of the mission school in which my wife and I are interested.

"Tell Howard and Kitty to be sure and come; they can put their visit a few weeks earlier as well as not.

"Oh, by the way, if you have heard from Ellis Holbrook lately, you are singing 'Glory Hallelujah' by this time!

"I am writing this in the counting room and am in a great hurry, though you wouldn't think it. Shall expect you by the third, *certainly*. Yours, etc.,

> *"Bob Turner."*

These letters came on Saturday evening. The next morning in Sabbath school, when the superintendent's bell rang, the minister left his class of mission scholars, and went up the aisle toward the altar, pausing first to speak with a bright-eyed little lady who sat before her class of bright-eyed little girls.

"Kitty, where is Howard?"

"At home, coaxing a fit of sick headache."

"Well, here are letters that will interest you both; came last evening—one contains an invitation. Tell Howard I think we must try to go. Mother bade me tell you she wanted to see you at the parsonage in the morning; she is not out today."

Then he went on. The scholars began to sit up straight and fold their arms; they knew they must listen if they wanted Mr. Lewis to talk to them. When every eye was fixed on him, he began:

"Children, I have a very short story to tell you today, about myself. Years ago, when I was a little boy, my Sabbath school teacher told us a story one morning which was the means of bringing me to Jesus. I have to thank that lady, next to God, that I am standing here today a minister of Christ. She was not our regular teacher, but was a stranger; I never saw her after that Sabbath. Perhaps you can imagine how I have longed, since I became a man and a minister, to find that lady and tell her what one hour of faithful teaching did for me. I thought it would help her, encourage her. I thought she would be likely to tell it to other teachers, and it would help them. But though I had it always in mind, and made very earnest efforts to find her, I never succeeded until last week. You know, children, it is ten years since I came here to be your pastor, and last week I learned that during all this time I have been living within twenty miles of the lady whom I have so long been seeking. And what else do you think I heard of her? Why, that two weeks ago she died. Scholars, my first thought was a sad one, that I never could thank her now. But you know I can; I expect to, one of these days. Why, when I get to heaven, one of the first things I shall do will be to seek her out and tell her about it. So, you see, she will know it, even if some of the watching angels up there have not told her already.

"Just here, I want to say one word to the teachers. This incident should come with wonderful encouragement to your hearts; reminding you that you may often speak words which spring up and bear fruit that reaches up to God. Though you do not know it, and *will* not until in heaven you take your crowns and question why there are so many stars.

"Children, next Sabbath I will tell you the story which led me to Christ; and all this week I am going to pray that it may have the same effect on some of my scholars.

"It is time now for your verse. If any of you can find out why what I have been telling you today made me think of this verse, you may tell me next Sabbath. Now repeat: 'Cast thy bread upon the waters: for thou shalt find it after many days.'"

THE END